The Cantatas of Luigi Rossi

Analysis and Thematic Index

Studies in Musicology

George Buelow, Series Editor
Professor of Musicology
Indiana University

Other Titles in This Series

The Canzone Villanesca Alla Napolitana *and Related Forms, 1537-1570* — Donna G. Cardamone

Valerio Dorico: Music Printer in Sixteenth-Century Rome — Suzanne G. Cusick

The Origins of Modern Musical Criticism: French and Italian Music, 1600-1750 — Georgia Cowart

Operas for the Papal Court, 1631-1668 — Margaret Murata

Passacaglio and Ciaccona: From Guitar Music to Italian Keyboard Variations in the 17th Century — Richard Hudson

The Spanish Baroque Guitar, Including a Transcription of Santiago de Murcia's Passacalles y obras, *(1732)* — Neil D. Pennington

Changing Aesthetic Views of Instrumental Music in 18th Century Germany — Bellamy Hosler

American Popular Stage Music, 1860-1880 — Deane L. Root

Henry Cowell's New Music, 1925-1936: The Society, the Music Editions, and the Recordings — Rita Mead

The Cantatas of Luigi Rossi

Analysis and Thematic Index

Vol. 2

by
Eleanor Caluori

umi
RESEARCH PRESS

Produced and distributed by
UMI Research Press
an imprint of
University Microfilms International
Ann Arbor, Michigan 48106

A revision of the author's thesis,
Brandeis University, 1971

Library of Congress Cataloging in Publication Data

Caluori, Eleanor.
The cantatas of Luigi Rossi.

(Studies in musicology ; no. 41)
Revision of thesis (Ph.D.)—Brandeis University, 1971.
Bibliography: p.
Includes index.
1. Rossi, Luigi, 1598-1653. Cantatas.   I. Title.
II. Series.

ML410.R76C3 1981   782.8'2'0924   81-4749
ISBN 0-8357-1171-4 (set)   AACR2
ISBN 0-8357-1192-7 (v.2)

Contents

Volume 2

Introduction   1

Thematic Index 1. Cantatas Attributed to Luigi Rossi
                 on Reliable Grounds   23

Thematic Index 2. Cantatas Attributed to Luigi Rossi
                 on Unreliable Grounds   145

Appendix   203
    Fragments from Luigi's Operas Included in Cantata
      Manuscripts
    Latin Pieces
    Musical Sources

Introduction

This catalogue provides the most accurate and comprehensive list of Luigi Rossi's cantatas yet compiled.[1] To accomplish this work, over two hundred manuscript collections of seventeenth-century cantatas were examined and collated. Two other catalogues of Luigi's cantatas have been previously published: Alfred Wotquenne, *Etude bibliographique sur le compositeur napolitain Luigi Rossi* (Brussels, 1909), and Alberto Ghislanzoni, *Luigi Rossi* (Milan, 1954), pp. 215-321; and their contents, after careful revision, are included with the addition of new information.

This catalogue, too, is part of the process of revaluation of the early Italian cantata. In the past one hundred years several anthologies of music and some collections of selected pieces by individual composers have been made available; articles have appeared sporadically disclosing newly found musical sources and biographical documents;[2] in 1914 an historical study, the *Geschichte der Weltlichen Solokantate*, by Eugen Schmitz, was published. By and large, however, the early Italian cantata is known primarily to scholars. Furthermore, only a small fraction of the several hundred cantatas composed by Carlo Caproli, Barbara Strozzi, Marco Marazzoli, Mario Savioni, Antonio Francesco Tenaglia, Orazio Michi, Marc'Antonio Pasqualini, and Giacomo Carissimi are known. Rarely is any performed in recital programs; a few have been recorded.[3] And Luigi's cantatas, which according to his contemporaries are the flowering of the genre, have fared no better. Although musicians have been neglectful of this repertory, musicologists have been reawakening interest in it. Recently various aspects of the cantata and the works of representative composers have been the subject of several doctoral dissertations.[4]

One of the first scholars to become actively interested in the Italian cantata was François Auguste Gevaert. He compiled the first catalogue of Luigi Rossi's cantatas, a list of sixty-three pieces in a manuscript notebook dating from about 1860.[5] Besides cataloguing Luigi's cantatas, Gevaert also copied, collected,[6] and published some of them, and is known to have had a few cantatas performed.[7] His anthology *Les Gloires d'Italie* (Paris, 1868) was the first publication containing pieces by Luigi to appear after the early eighteenth-century *Recueil de Ballard* (Paris, 1708) which has three duets by Luigi, two without attribution. While

Gevaert's investigations are limited, and for the most part unpublished, they remain important for having laid the foundation for subsequent studies.

After Gevaert, Eitner in his encyclopedic *Quellen-Lexikon* (1900-1904)[8] gave a brief account of Luigi's music, mentioning in particular Gevaert's transcriptions of Luigi's cantatas. But Eitner was unaware of Gevaert's handwritten catalogue of the cantatas, for in his summary list of Luigi's music he omits most of the sources indicated by Gevaert. Eitner does, however, draw attention to new sources.[9] The *Quellen-Lexikon* does not list the cantatas individually by text incipits, except for a few; instead, it lists them collectively with only a reference to their location. While Eitner presents new information, he unfortunately lists several compositions[10] at the Milan Conservatory and at the Gesellschaft der Musikfreunde in Vienna that are not by Luigi but by the nineteenth-century composer Luigi Felice Rossi.

Eitner's account of Luigi's life and works, although cursory and incomplete, was important, for it summarized most of the research done up to his time.

Gevaert's work was continued by his friend and pupil Alfred Wotquenne who in 1909 was the first to publish a catalogue of Luigi's music. Of the two hundred and twenty-six items Wotquenne lists, all but six are Italian cantatas that he found in seventy-five manuscripts and in five printed collections.[11] Although he personally examined most of the sources given in his *Etude bibliographique*, Wotquenne did not see the manuscripts which he lists at the Christ Church, the Casanatense, and the Vatican libraries; there are, consequently, a number of gaps and errors in the *Etude*. For example, Wotquenne could not identify the five cantatas seen by Gevaert at the Casanatense and listed by him in his handwritten catalogue.[12] Also, several of the anonymous concordances in Christ Church and Vatican manuscripts which Wotquenne gives are not concordances at all but altogether different pieces.[13] Finally, not realizing that the attributions "luigi" in most of the Christ Church manuscripts are not reliable because the attributions, in a hand different from the hands of the texts, were probably added by someone after the manuscripts had been compiled, Wotquenne ascribes to Luigi all the pieces in question. Some of these pieces are, in fact, elsewhere attributed to Luigi, but many pieces have concordances attributing them to other composers, and these attributions prove to be reliable. Despite the errors, Wotquenne's *Etude* is an excellent investigation of many manuscript sources, and it lists much of Luigi's music. In addition to his bibliographical study, Wotquenne aided in disseminating and preserving the music, copying with accuracy many of the cantatas in the sources he examined. The several large volumes[14] in his clear, fine hand are an important part of the Italian cantata collection at the Conservatoire Royale de Musique at Bruxelles.

It is primarily Wotquenne's copies of Luigi's cantatas which form the basis of Hugo Riemann's brief study in the *Handbuch der Musikgeschichte*, 2d ed. (Leipzig, 1922), II/2, 372-383. In Riemann's list of Luigi's cantatas the one hundred pieces examined at the Brussels library are divided into several groups according to form. Within each group the pieces are arranged alphabetically (except for one group in which the duets and a trio are listed at the end of the group with some deviation from the alphabetical order), and the numbering throughout is consecutive. Although Riemann does not acknowledge the source of the concordances he gives for each item, they are taken from Wotquenne's catalogue. It is probable, too, that Wotquenne's copies are the sources for two cantatas by Luigi which he published in his *Kantaten-Frühling* (Leipzig, ca. 1910).[15] Riemann's is not a bibliographical contribution, but rather an analytical study of the music, and as such, despite its limitations, it is valuable. Above all, it is the first modern discussion of Luigi's music.

During the early part of this century bibliographical studies continued, and their results were published in several articles by Alberto Cametti and Henry Prunières in 1912 and 1913. The significance of Cametti's investigation of manuscripts in the library of Principe D. Mario Chigi Albani (now part of the Chigi *fondo* at the Vatican library) and in the Casanatense library lies in the fact that he uncovered eleven new sources.[16] Consequently he was able to add to Wotquenne's *Etude* eight new pieces as well as concordances for seventeen cantatas. (Two of the new pieces are not properly cantatas, one being part of the oratorio *Il Peccatore Pentito*; the other, a solo Latin motet.)[17] And Prunières also found eight new manuscript sources in the Naples Conservatory library and was able to offer sixteen new cantatas besides eight concordances for those already known.[18]

In order to appreciate the work of Cametti and Prunières, one must consider the severe restrictions under which their investigations in the Italian libraries were made. Prunières reports that during his visit to the Naples Conservatory library in 1909 he was not permitted to copy anything. Cametti was allowed to examine three manuscripts at the Casanatense for his 1913 study, but many others were inaccessible to him.[19] The library's policy was not consistent, however, for in 1912, the year before Cametti published his study, Ludwig Landshoff published two cantatas by Luigi from another manuscript in the same Casanatense library.[20] In fact, one of these cantatas, *Non la volete intendere*, had not been catalogued when it was published.[21] The second piece, *Che sventura, son tant'anni*, existing in manuscripts in other libraries, was known to Wotquenne in a French and an Oxford source, and to Prunières in a Neapolitan source. The Casanatense concordance indicated by Landshoff, however, is listed for the first time in this catalogue (see nos. 36 and 126).[22]

Besides finding new sources of Luigi's cantatas, both Prunières and Cametti found important biographical documents the contents of which they reported in several articles.[23] Prunières, moreover, published six cantatas by Luigi in 1914[24] and two more in 1922.[25] Landshoff, too, published more pieces by Luigi in 1927;[26] and in both his 1912 and 1927 editions he scrupulously describes his manuscript sources, a practice disregarded by most editors until recently. Regrettably Prunières neglected to identify the manuscript sources of the cantatas he published; the source of one of them, *S'io son vinto*, was unknown at the first printing of this catalogue.[27] But a few years ago, during his investigation of the cantata manuscript holdings of many European libraries, Owen Jander found the MS 3372 at the library of Sainte-Geneviève in Paris with this cantata attributed to Luigi Rossi. No doubt MS 3372 was Prunières' source.

Prunières's commitment to the furthering of knowledge and appreciation of the music of Luigi and his colleagues was unsurpassed by that of any of the other pioneers in this area of research. His articles and books on seventeenth-century music and musicians are still important.[28] His essay "La cantate italienne à voix seule au dix-septième siècle" is a basic study and gives an excellent critical evaluation of the subject.[29]

The most recent study of Luigi Rossi is Alberto Ghislanzoni's *Luigi Rossi. Biografia e Analisi Delle Composizioni* (1954). In the "Catalogo delle Canzoni, Arie e Cantate," pp. 215-321, an appendix to the biographical and historical essay, Ghislanzoni presents the results of the investigations outlined above without correction or revision. He also, of course, offers new material. There are three hundred eighty-eight items attributed definitively to Luigi: two instrumental pieces, six Latin cantatas, and three hundred eighty Italian cantatas. If this catalogue is examined carefully, however, the total number of Italian cantatas that are actually by Luigi proves to be much smaller. For one thing, Ghislanzoni lists several cantatas twice: 297=310, 306=369, 359=377; 152 is part of 153, 156 is part of 288, and 212 is part of 66. One of these, *Lasciate ch'io peni* (359=377), being part of the larger "Oratorio-Cantata" *Il Peccator Pentito*, described by Ghislanzoni in a separate chapter of his book (pp. 112-115), does not properly belong in the catalogue. Ghislanzoni also includes *Purche lo sappi tu*, a duet that may be Carlo Caproli's despite the fact that Wotquenne lists it under "Oeuvres douteuses ou apocryphes." Then, perhaps not realizing that the attribution is a later addition, Ghislanzoni places *Mi dispiace dirl'bomiè* in his catalogue although Prunières did not mention it among the pieces attributed to Luigi in the Naples MS 33.4.15 (probably because the attribution had not yet been added). Finally, Ghislanzoni includes most of the pieces in the Vatican manuscripts Barberini lat. 4175, 4200, and 4208, and some in Barb. lat. 4204. Of all of these pieces, however, only one has the attribution Luigi Rossi; the others are anonymous or bear the initials MAP (see pp. 6 and 7, below).

Ghislanzoni's reasons for claiming so many pieces for Luigi are not substantial. He says, "... il controllo calligrafico suffragato, avvalorato da altri dati ed elementi, ci ha consentito di riconoscere come di Luigi Rossi un numero notevole di pezzi colà privi del nome dell'autore, in quanto erano proprio i fascicoli stilati dalla mano del Maestro, e fors'anche della moglie, in brutte copie o buone copie" (p. 216). There is no proof, however, that the hands of Barb. lat. 4175, 4200, 4204, and 4208 are either Luigi's or his wife's. Comparison of these manuscripts with one another and with the facsimiles of Luigi's will (the first of Ghislanzoni's "Documentazioni," p. 184) and Costanza's letter (facing p. 65) reveals that the hands are not the same.

Concerning the hand of Barb. lat. 4208 Ghislanzoni refers back to his description of Barb. lat. 4200: "La calligrafia uniforme in tutti fa suppore che l'intero fascicolo sia autografo" (p. 218); he says that these remarks are also valid for Barb. lat. 4201 and 4203. Likewise, he believes that the hand of Barb. lat. 4204 "si può ritenere un autografo"[30] and that of Barb. lat. 4374 "appare un autografo" (p. 218). Whose "autografo" does Ghislanzoni mean? The hands of these manuscripts are not alike. Only those of Barb. lat. 4201 and 4203 resemble one another. Moreover Barb. lat. 4204 is the work of several copyists.

Ghislanzoni does not use the MS Add. 30491 at the British Musuem, supposedly Luigi's autograph,[31] in comparing Luigi's hand with the hands in the Barberini manuscripts. Perhaps Add. 30491 is poor material for comparison since it was begun at least twenty years before the earliest Barberini manuscripts.[32] Nevertheless, examination of the hand of the solo pieces in Add. 30491, which were added some time later,[33] reveals a similarity between it and the hand of ff. 59v-96v and 102v-105 of Barb. lat. 4175. Ghislanzoni, however, believes that Luigi's hand appears on other folios in the volume. *Dove mi spingi, amor*, ff. 45v-49, is according to him "in calligrafia autografo di L.R." (p. 216). But it is the hand on ff. 59v-96v and 102v-105 that seems more like Luigi's hand as it appears in the will of 1646. Ghislanzoni still believes that the music was copied by Luigi, and accounts for the different hands as the result of copying which was sometimes careful, sometimes hurried.[34] Ghislanzoni was also influenced by the inscription at the front of the volume "Ce livre apartien a mon pere mons. Louigii," and by the fact that many of the pieces (about a quarter of the contents) are attributable to Luigi by concordances.

Even if the volume had belonged to Luigi, its contents need not be exclusively his compositions. In fact, there are concordances with the attribution Pasqualini for several;[35] most of these cantatas are on the folios following f. 105 which Ghislanzoni says, "scritte in calligrafia ottima e diversa, danno l'impressione d'essere state riempite in epoca posteriore" (p. 217). Among the pieces on these folios, however, is also a cantata attributed to Luigi in a Casanatense manuscript.[36]

As for Luigi's hand, if it does appear in Barb. lat. 4175, then Barb. lat. 4208, 4201, 4219, 4220, 4221, 4222, 4203, 4223, and 4374 are the "autografi" of other people, for the hand of ff. 59v-96v and 102v-105 does not resemble any of these "autografi."

Ghislanzoni's arguments based on false analysis of the handwritings cannot be taken seriously. Consequently there is no justification for the inclusion in his catalogue of eighty-eight anonymous pieces as unequivocally Luigi's. His conjectures have proved correct in some cases, for concordances with the attribution Luigi have since been found for several of the pieces. But it can also be proved that some of these eighty-eight cantatas were composed by Carissimi, Carlo Caproli, Marco Marazzoli, Marc'Antonio Pasqualini, and Antonio Francesco Tenaglia. The other cantatas for which concordances with attributions have not been found must remain anonymous. They are listed in this catalogue under "Cantatas attributed to Luigi on unreliable grounds."

Besides these anonymous pieces, Ghislanzoni also ascribes to Luigi several pieces which appear in the same Barberini sources with the initials MAP. These initials, which occur sporadically in Barb. lat. 4175, 4150, 4168, 4200, 4203, 4222, 4223 (in the first two manuscripts only once, in the others more frequently), and at the beginning of Barb. lat. 4219, 4220 and 4221, refer to Marc'Antonio Pasqualini. This colleague of Luigi in the employ of Cardinal Antonio Barberini was famous for his singing and was also known as a composer.[37] Ghislanzoni, believing "MAP" to be a reference to the interpreter and not to the composer,[38] includes in his catalogue four pieces (*Chiuda quest'occhi*, *Su la rota della fortuna*, *Navicella che si altera* and *Io ritorno dal periglio*), giving no proof that they are Luigi's nor any that their attribution MAP refers to the interpreter. There is good reason to believe, however that the attribution MAP refers in general to the composer.[39] Concordances in many manuscripts indicate that the music is "Del Sig. Marc'Antonio Pasqualini," or simply "Del Pasqualini."[40]

It is difficult to find an example that might give basis to Ghislanzoni's reasoning. The aria *Dove mi spingi, amor* from Luigi's *Il Palazzo Incantata* might be such an example. In the cantata MS Barb. lat. 4223 the ascription "MAP Poesia N.N. AB" is placed above the aria, seeming to refer to the interpreter since Pasqualini did sing *Dove mi spingi* at the first performance of the opera.[41] And because the scores and libretti[42] of *Il Palazzo Incantato* contain the aria, it is reasonable to assume that Luigi composed it.

On the other hand, the precise ascription "musica del S. Marcantonio Pasqualini is placed above this same aria in the Casanatense MS 2467. The attributions in this manuscript being reliable, one is tempted to give credence to this one. Thus it may well be that this particular aria from *Il Palazzo Incantato* was composed by the singer himself. It was not uncommon for various numbers of an opera to be composed or recomposed by another without acknowledgement of the fact in the score. In Mazzocchi's *La Catena d'Adone*, for example, the part of Adonis was recomposed by Sigismondo d'India and published under Mazzocchi's name.[43] Alessandro Stradella is known to have composed numerous substitute arias, as well as prologues and intermezzi, for Roman productions of operas substantially by other composers.[44] In a performance of Cesti's *Orontea* the anonymous aria *No, no, fuggir non vo* may have been inserted, since the text is found in the Venetian libretto of 1666 (see below, no. 358). There are, no doubt, other examples that might be cited; and many more will be uncovered when the arias from the operas are collated with the arias in cantata manuscripts.[45]

The case of *Dove mi spingi, amor* also exemplifies the problem: can the attribution in a manuscript source refer to the performer? There is no proof that it can, for in none of the many volumes of cantatas that I examined is there a direct reference to the interpreter. Therefore, while it is possible, it is unlikely that Ghislanzoni's interpretation of the initials MAP is correct.

Although the total number of cantatas that can be ascribed with assurance to Luigi is considerably smaller than the three hundred eighty Ghislanzoni lists, it is nevertheless larger than the sum of those listed by Wotquenne and those discovered by Cametti and Prunières, for besides the Barberini manuscripts two other new sources of Luigi's music are presented in Ghislanzoni's catalogue. In the MS D 2357 at the Florence Conservatory library Ghislanzoni found many hitherto unknown duets attributed to Luigi, some available in no other source. He also found one new cantata, and concordances for several others already known, in the MS A-5-Cass at the Genoa Conservatory library. These discoveries, his investigation of the Barberini manuscripts, his correction of Celani's indices of these manuscripts,[46] and his organization of all previous studies are Ghislanzoni's major contributions.

In order to make corrections in the previous catalogues, to check the reliability of the attributions, and to find new concordances, it was necessary to make a thorough study of all the manuscripts containing the mid-century repertory and of some containing later pieces. Among the more than two hundred manuscripts examined, ninety-six are new sources of Luigi's music. And in these manuscripts forty-six new pieces by Luigi have been recovered. In addition, I am able to offer for the cantatas already known numerous anonymous concordances and many with attributions, some confirming Luigi's authorship, others contesting it. Moreover, it has been possible to find two and sometimes more settings of a text, thus making interesting material available for comparative study.

To determine the relative accuracy of the attributions the entire contents of all the manuscripts were collated, and the handwritings of the attributions were compared to the hands of the texts. But still difficulties were encountered. For instance, MS Q 44 at the Bologna Civico Museo, whose attributions in the hand of the copyist are in most instances proved correct by concordances, has the trio *Al bel lume d'un volto* with the attribution Luigi Rossi; the same trio is anonymous in Barb. lat. 4204, a manuscript which bears the curious inscription "Stracciafoglio d'un amante che non ama," as do the manuscripts Barb. lat 4205, 4219, 4220, 4221, 4222, and 4223, manuscripts containing the same repertory as Barb. lat. 4204. This whole complex of manuscripts is problematic because no composers' names appear in them except occasionally the initials MAP. These initials seem to indicate that the inscription refers to the castrato Marc'Antonio Pasqualini and that the volumes belonged to him. It is highly probable that most of the music contained in these manuscripts are his compositions.[47] It is also possible that some are by Luigi Rossi, his close friend and colleague.[48] All except three of the concordances found for the cantatas in these volumes are either anonymous or are attributed to Pasqualini. But the three exceptional concordances name Luigi Rossi the composer.[49] Since there is no conclusive evidence proving it incorrect, I decided to give credence to the attribution in Q 44.

On stylistic grounds one of the pieces in this complex of Barberini manuscripts was thought by Einstein to be Rossi's. Landshoff, who published this piece, while admitting the possibility of Rossi's or of Carissimi's authorship, believes that there is more evidence in favor of Giovanni Legrenzi as the probable composer (see no. 409 in this catalogue). The point is that in the case at hand one cannot prove, on stylistic evidence alone, that the contents of these manuscripts are the work of Pasqualini, or Rossi, or any other composer.

Of the many pieces with questionable attributions numerous ones might be attributed to Luigi on stylistic grounds if his musical vocabulary were not so much the same as that of his contemporaries, who also used the devices of minor-major change, hemiola, quadruple measures in sections of triple meter, melismas toward the cadence, the octave leap at the beginning of a phrase, the dominant chord over the tonic pedal in recitatives, the échappée at the cadence, et al. To be sure, it is the way in which the means are used and how they are combined—it is the *quality* of the choices made—that marks a composer's style. Nonetheless, even after long and intimate knowledge of his music it is impossible to determine unequivocally whether a composer may or may not have made the choices that created an anonymous piece. In this catalogue, therefore, no attributions have been made on stylistic grounds.

Luigi's cantatas are collected in this catalogue in two groups, those whose attribution is reliable, and those whose attribution is questionable. The cantatas of the first group are for the most part in seventeenth-century manuscripts and have the attribution in the hand of the copyist; a few are cantatas attributed to Luigi in seventeenth-century publications.[50]

An exception in this first group is *Horche la notte del silenzio* (no. 87), a cantata by Luigi mentioned in a letter by his contemporary Pietro della Valle, but the only extant source of which bears no attribution. Other exceptions are *V'è, v'è che miro?* (no. 201), *Sospiri, sù, sù!* (no. 180), and *Non la volete intendetere* (no. 126) in the MS 2466 at the Casanatense. Although these three cantatas have attributions that are not in the hands of their texts, they are included in this first group because their attributions are in a hand that is contemporary, that of another copyist of the same manuscript.

In the second group are: cantatas which in various catalogues have been attributed to Luigi either by error or on uncertain grounds; several ensembles listed with the attribution Luigi in an eighteenth-century catalogue, but of which the manuscript source has not yet been found; cantatas attributed to Luigi having concordances, but with conflicting attributions; and cantatas which bear attributions not in the hand of the text, and of doubtful reliability.

Many of the cantatas in a number of manuscripts in the Christ Church library (MSS 946, 947, 948, 949, 950, 951, and 952) are of this last group. Often the attribution "sig luigi" (the initial letters are usually not capitalized) is added in a hand that does not match any of the hands in which the texts are copied.[51] In a large volume of ensembles, MS 996 in the Christ Church collection, the same attribution appears (on folios 73, 112, and 139), here obviously a later and superfluous addition since the copyist had given Luigi's name at the beginning of the fascicles containing his music.

Five of the cantatas that were placed in the first group in the first publication of this catalogue proved to be by Marco Marazzoli (Thematic

Index 2, nos. 326, 396, 416, 430, and 433). An index of his music drawn up by the composer was brought to light by the investigations of Wolfgang Witzenmann.[52] The MSS Chigi Q V 68-69, Q VI 80-81, and Q VIII 177-191 in the Vatican library lack Marazzoli's name, but are in his hand; they contain the bulk of his vocal chamber music. Two of the anonymous cantatas in Barb. lat. 4208 included by Ghislanzoni among Luigi's cantatas are in the Marazzoli manuscripts (Thematic Index 2, nos. 335 and 387).

Also included in the second group is a setting of Cav. Marino's *Stabat Mater* attributed to Orazio dell' Arpa in one source and anonymous in two others. This extant setting may possibly be the same as the one attributed to Luigi in the lost MS Magl. XIX.22 formerly at the Biblioteca Nazionale, and would thus come under the third category. It is also possible, however, that both Luigi and Orazio made settings of the same poem; the setting attributed to Luigi is thus also listed in the first group, marked as lost. It is numbered only in the second group.

Considering the facts thus far documented, one is struck by the need for continued research of the sources. The division of cantatas into those whose attribution is reliable and those whose attribution is doubtful must be subject to constant revision. Further study is necessary, especially of the Barberini "Stracciafogli."

Text Incipit

Repetitions are omitted if the text is a poem in whose original structure such repetitions would not occur. The spelling in the sources is retained; text variants are noted beside the source in which they appear; the punctuation, usually omitted in the sources, is mostly the writer's. The text incipit is longer than in most catalogues in order to avoid ambiguity. Often cantatas begin with the same few words, but continue with a different text, for example:

> "Si, v'ingannate, se di Fortuna il crine"
> "Si, v'ingannate, si! Io senza la mercede"
> "Olà, pensieri, olà! Il varco del mio core"
> "Olà, pensieri, e qual dentro al mio seno"
> "Mortale, che pensi? Son caduchi i tuoi trionfi"
> "Mortale, e che pensi? Viver secoli immensi"
> "Ho perso il mio core, chi l'ha melo dia"
> "Ho perso il mio core per vaga beltà"
> "Ho perso il mio core, e chi con frode rapito me l'ha"

References to previous catalogues

The abbreviations Wo., Gh., and Re., followed by a number, refer to the location of the cantata in the catalogues by Alfred Wotquenne and Alberto Ghislanzoni, and in the list included in Hugo Riemann's *Handbuch*.

Music incipit

Complete incipits had to be forfeited in order to keep publishing costs low. It is regrettable that only the upper voice can be given, for the addition of the other part or parts would not merely satisfy a musical aesthetic, but would offer a complete musical example for study.

The incipits retain the original clefs placed on the staff as in the original sources, indicating thereby the voice quality and the range for which the piece is composed. The original note values,[53] key and mensural signatures are kept. A few times the writer added accidentals in parentheses. These additions are based on the writer's study of the notational practices of the time, and of the idiosyncracies of individual copyists.

In scores of this period, as is well known,[54] the accidental affects only the note it precedes[55] and the immediate repetitions of that note. A bar-line, on the other hand, does not ordinarily cancel an accidental.[56]

This general rule already begins to dissolve, however, for there are times when the accidental is not invalidated by a single intervening note. One note a second or a third distant, or two auxiliary tones, or a passing tone and a chord tone connected in a ligature to the note with the accidental and its repetition may intervene without cancelling the accidental.[57] Usually the intervening tones are ornamental, or of brief time value, and usually the repeated note before which the accidental is implied retains the function of the first note.

Most often, however, the copyists adhere to the general rule and reiterate the accidental. Also, apparently unsure of the validity of the accidental for immediate repetitions of a note, they sometimes use superfluous accidentals, scrupulously inserting an accidental before a repeated note after a bar-line or within a measure after a silence. There are even a few examples where the accidental is replaced before each repeated note.[58] Yet on one page, or in various copies of a page, there are both examples of scrupulousness and of negligent omissions. For example, in one source of *Pene, pianti*, 248, a flat is placed before each E in the second measure; in another source the second flat is omitted, while in two other sources the first is omitted and the second is present.

While the copyists are often careful to replace accidentals, they are not concerned with making cancellations evident. In general the cancellation of a preceding accidental is noted only when a chromatic step is involved.[59] In all other cases an intervening note is sufficient.[60] Even where the situation seems ambiguous to us the copyists do not mark the change.

In the incipit *Che pretendente*, 214, for example, the second E in the second measure is still raised, for the accidental is not cancelled by the intervening auxiliary—but the third E is no longer altered. This E is not a leading tone to F and a chord tone, as were the previous E's, but is the 4th degree of B-flat in a temporary modulation to that tonality and acts as an ornamental tone. As the measure appears in the sources the one accidental at its beginning might erroneously be extended to all the E's. In another example, from the cantata *Gelosia*, 78, no accidental is placed before the last A of the following phrase:

Strophes 1a & 2a

la-sciami ge-lo- si - a—

It may appear that the flat is valid for this A also, since occasionally the accidental is not reinstated after the intervention of one tone. But there are factors which indicate that the general rule must be followed. The A is not flat. First of all, the A does not retain the function of the preceding A flat. It is no longer an appoggiatura to G, but a passing tone to B-flat. Secondly, the G that intervenes is not an ornamental tone, nor is it of brief duration. Finally, the false relation between A-flat (if the flat were repeated) and the fifth of the dominant chord that follows is not typical of the style. Although in the third strophe the copyists scrupulously mark the replacement of the flat after the bar, they see no need to indicate the cancellation.

Strophe 3a

la- scia-mi ge - lo - si - a —

Other problems regarding accidentals, perhaps lesser known, concern situations in which the accidental was unintentionally omitted by the copyist. Since these situations appear time and time again, they can be easily defined. In pieces *finalis* on B-flat, C, or G, and with only a B-flat in the signature, and in pieces with D *finalis* and with no flat in the signature, the flat before E is sometimes intended, but not provided.[61] Likewise, in pieces with *finalis* on E, A, D, or G, but without signature accidentals, the sharp before F is sometimes intended, but not provided.[62] Also in pieces with D *finalis* and with no accidental in the signature, or only F-sharp, the sharp before C can sometimes be inferred.[63]

These key signatures, a vestige of hexachordal and modal thinking, were inadequate to notate the new tonally directed compositions. The B-flat, which was once used to indicate the *hexachordum molle*[64] and to designate transposed modes,[65] is the most common signature in this period.[66] Almost as frequent is the absence of any signature accidental. Thus it was necessay to add accidentals in the course of the music.

Although the copyists frequently took care to insert these accidentals, it is not unusual to find at least several omitted in the course of a piece. Most often the omissions occur before ornamental tones or before notes in "passaggi" of relatively brief duration.[67]

That the accidental is required in these situations is indicated by various musical and notational clues. Sometimes the melodic phrase, where the accidental is omitted, reappears in the bass line with the accidental present,[68] or the melodic motive refers back to a preceding phrase.[69] In some cases the omission of the accidental would cause an unstylistic augmented second[70] or an unintended false relation.[71] In other cases the change of function of the tone indicates the necessity for the accidental.[72] Also, recurring idioms precisely noted in the same work or in other works reveal where accidentals are required.[73] Even more obvious clues are the presence of the accidental below the continuo part or in another voice, or in the bass line. Occasionally the accidental comes immediately after the note. This happens, as in the fourth measure of *Non m'affligete più*,

127, with an anticipation of brief time value, or as in the second measure of *Al soave spirar*, 11, with a passing tone that anticipates the chord tone on the next pulse. Finally, if concordances are available, these sometimes have the accidental or its equivalent (in the case of a concordance in a variant key).

Two incipits are given for the few cantatas with variant openings. If a cantata is extant in more than one tonality, this is indicated beside the source which varies from the tonality of the incipit.

Attribution

The attributions in this catalogue are given exactly as they appear in the sources. Only the words "Del Sig." are omitted. "Del Sig." or "Musica di" precedes the name of the composer in most manuscripts. Very often the attribution is placed at the beginning of the cantata, but in a few manuscripts it is placed at the end of the volume in the list of contents. In some manuscripts one finds the designation "del d°" (del medesimo) referring to the composer of the previous piece. Eleven successive pieces in the MS G 885 at the Conservatorio Santa Cecilia have this designation, but the first piece in the manuscript with the attribution to which "del d°" refers is missing! Since the remaining fragment, however, is the final twenty-one measures of *Dove, dove più miro* attributed to Luigi in a Casanatense manuscript, and since several other pieces of the group can be attributed with certainty to Luigi, the entire eleven pieces and the fragment must be Luigi's.

The author of the text is rarely mentioned; whenever this information is available, it is marked next to the source that gives it.

Sources

Manuscript sources are listed first; the modern copies in the Brussels Conservatory library and in the Einstein notebooks are listed next; following are the printed sources, the earlier publications preceding the modern ones. The sigla used to indicate the location of the sources are listed in the Appendix; they are adopted from *Répertoire International des Sources Musicales*. References to modern published sources are also abbreviated; these abbreviations are also indicated in the Appendix.

Notes for the Introduction

1. It first appeared in the now out-of-print *Wellesley Edition Cantata Index Series* (abbreviated *WECIS*), fascicles 3a and 3b, 1965. This series, published by Wellesley College,

was directed by Owen Jander, an energetic, enthusiastic scholar-musician who not only ably coordinated the publication, but did the copying of the music incipits and the printing. I have retained his copies of the incipits in the present publications. Four other indices were published: *Antonio Cesti* (fasc. 1, 1964), compiled by David Burrows; *Mario Savioni* (fasc. 2, 1964), compiled by Irving Eisley; *Giacomo Carissimi* (fasc. 5, 1966), compiled by Gloria Rose and *Alessandro Stradella* (fascicles 4a and 4b, 1969), compiled by Owen Jander.

2. Only those relevant to this study are listed in the Bibliography.

3. *Storia della Musica Italiana*, vol. II contains examples of early seventeenth-century vocal music; most are opera excerpts, but a few are solo and ensemble cantatas. The composer best represented is Marco Marazzoli. A more recent recording of cantatas is *Chamber Music for Soprano and Continuo*, Pleiades Records, P103.

4. C. Sites, "Benedetto Marcello's Chamber Cantatas" (University of North Carolina, 1959); Gloria Rose, "The Cantatas of Carissimi" (Yale University, 1959); David Burrows, "The Cantatas of Antonio Cesti" (Brandeis University, 1961); Owen Jander, "The Works of Alessandro Stradella Related to the Cantata and the Opera" (Harvard University, 1962); Edwin Hanley, "Alessandro Scarlatti's *Cantate da Camera*; A Bibliographical Study" (Yale University, 1963); Irving Eisley, "The Secular Cantatas of Mario Savioni" (University of California, Los Angeles, 1964); Gordon Crain, "The Vocal Music of Bernardo Pasquini" (Yale University, 1966); Iva Moore Buff, "The Chamber Duets and Trios of Carissimi" (Univeristy of Rochester, 1973); Kathleen Chaikin, "The Solo Cantatas of Alessandro Stradella" (Stanford Univeristy, 1975); Colin Timms, "The Chamber Duets of Agostino Steffani" (University of London, 1976).

5. The sixty-three pieces listed by Gevaert in MS XY 8286, pp. 65-71, at the Brussels Conservatory library are extant in seven manuscripts in the British Museum, the Bibliothèque Royale de Bruxelles, the Bibliothèque Nationale in Paris, and the Casanatensc in Rome, Gevaert's notebook also contains a list of Carissimi cantatas (probably the first) and copies of many cantatas by seventeenth-century Italian composers.

6. Gevaert copied the music in the MSS XY 8286, F 663 and F 664 at the Brussels Conservatory. He also realized the continuo for the eighteen pieces in F 663 and F 664. For the Brussels Conservatory library Gevaert also purchased the MS F 662, a large collection of duets, trios, and quartets, all but one by Luigi, copied in England during the first half of the eighteenth century.

7. Before the publication of *Les Gloires*, at the meetings of the Société des Compositeurs de Musique in Paris in 1866, Gevaert had some of Luigi's cantatas performed by the famous singer Salvator Marchesi de Castrone; see Wotquenne, *Etude*, p. 111.

8. Robert Eitner, *Biographisch-Bibliographisches Quellen-Lexikon* . . . (Leipzig, 1900-1904), VII, 323-324.

9. Eitner refers the reader to Gaetano Gaspari's *Catalogo della Biblioteca del Liceo Musicale di Bologna* (Bologna, 1890-) for compositions by Luigi Rossi at that library. This catalogue, however, lists only a few of the pieces attributed to Luigi in the library's manuscripts. Eitner indicates that there are three pieces by Luigi in manuscripts at the

Biblioteca Estense in Modena, and that at Oxford, in the Christ Church library manuscripts, there are one hundred and twelve cantatas attributed to Luigi. He also draws attention to the manuscripts F 662 and F 694 (=F. A.VI.38) at the Brussels Conservatory library, to Chigi Q IV 13 at the Vatican, to Harl. 1501 and 1863 (olim 59 and 64) at the British Museum. Besides these manuscript sources, Eitner also lists three seventeenth-century publications in which there are pieces by Luigi: those of 1640, 1646, and 1679 (see Appendix p. 210).

10. A Litany for three voices with orchestra and a duet for two sopranos and various instruments at the Milan Conservatory; a Mass, a Tantum ergo, and four numbers from the opera *Gli Avventurieri* at the library of the Gesellschaft. About Luigi Felice, see Carlo Schmidl, *Dizionario Universale dei Musicisti* (Milan, 1929), II, 403.

11. These sources are in the British Musuem; Christ Church, Oxford; the Fitzwilliam Museum, Cambridge; the Bibliothèque Royale, Bruxelles; the Conservatoire Royale de Bruxelles; the Kassel Landesbibliothek; the Mecklenburgische Landesbibliothek; the Oesterreichische Nationalbibliothek, Wien; the Bibliothèque Nationale, Paris; the Civico Museo Bibliografico Musicale (*olim* Liceo Musicale), Bologna; the Casanatense library, Rome; the Biblioteca Estense, Modena, and the Vatican library.

12. *Mai nol dirò, Partii dal gioire, Quanto è credulo, Non sarà, non fù, Da perfida speranza* (nos. 112, 141, 157, 131, and 52 in this catalogue).

13. *Che volete da me, Non mi fate mentire, O dura più d'un sasso* (nos. 311, 128, and 135 in this catalogue). Norman Smith, "The Cantatas of Luigi Rossi; the Christ Church Manuscripts," unpublished seminar paper (Yale University, 1955), mentions three pieces by Luigi in the MSS 377, 17, and 948 which Wotquenne did not know about.

14. MSS 17193, 17196, 17197, and 15261.

15. *Se peni tuo danno* and *S'era alquanto addormentato*.

16. Alberto Cametti, "Alcuni documenti inediti su la vita di Luigi Rossi compositore di musica (1597-1653)," *SIMG*, XIV (1912-13), pp. 1-26. Most of the article concerns biographical documents, one of which Purnières had already published in 1910, *SIMG*, XII, p. 13; the musical sources are described on pages 18-19. Cametti also published a thematic catalogue of the cantatas by Orazio Michi, based primarily on the contents of MS 2490 at the Casanatense. The catalogue is appended to Cametti's fine documentary article "Orazio Michi 'Dell'Arpa'," *RMI*, XXI (1914), pp. 203-277.

17. *Lasciate ch'io peni* and *O amantissime Jesù*.

18. Henry Prunières, "Notes bibliographiques sur les cantates de Luigi Ross au Conservatoire de Naples," *ZIMG*, XIV (1913), pp. 109-111. Of the sixteen cantatas only one, the duet *Che più far degg'io*, cannot be attributed to Luigi with certitude since it is attributed to Arcangelo (del Leuto) in a manuscript in Bologna. (See no. 412 in this catalogue.)

19. For example, he was not able to find the source of the five cantatas by Gevaert at this library which has since become available and can be identified as MS 2468.

20. Ludwig Landshoff (ed.), *Alte Meister des Bel Canto. Eine Sammlung von Arien aus Opera und Kantalen, . . .* (Leipzig, 1912).

21. It is not included in Ghislanzoni's catalogue of 1953.

22. The two cantatas published by Landshoff are mentioned by Norman Smith in the seminar paper cited above, where he lists them under "Rossi Compositions in Modern Editions" (a group of nineteen pieces).

23. See note 16. Also Alberto Cametti, "Luigi Rossi, organista a San Luigi dei Francesi," *La Critica Musicale*, vol. II (Florence, 1919), pp. 16-20; Henry Prunières, "Les representations du Palazzo d'Atalante à Rome (1642) d'après des documents inedits," *SIMG*, XIV (1912-13), pp. 218-226; idem, *L'Opera italien en France avant Lulli* (Paris, 1913); idem, "Les musiciens du Cardinal Antonio Barberini," *Mélanges de Musicologie offerts à M. Lionel del la Laurencie* (Paris, 1933), pp. 117-122.

24. *Six Airs et Une Passacaille de Luigi Rossi* (Paris, 1914). The cantatas are *Se dolente e flebile cetra; S'io son vinto, occhi; Diva, tu ch'in trono assisa: lo ero pargoletta; Sulla veglia d'una speme,* and *Così va, dice il mio core*. The first four were also published in the *Suppléments au Monde musical* of February 15 and 28, 1913 (Paris).

25. Prunières and G. Tailleferre (eds.), *Les Maîtres du Chant*, vol. III (Paris, 1924-1927). Besides the two cantatas *lo che sin hor le piante* and *Fate quel che volete*, the aria *Mio ben, teco il tormento* from Luigi's *Orfeo* is also in this edition.

26. *Alte Meister des Bel Canto. Italienische Kammerduette des 17. and 18. Jahrhunderts* (Leipzig, 1927), pp. 66-92. The pieces by Luigi are *A te, mio core: Poichè mancò speranza; Si o no, dissi al mio core; Speranza al tuo pallore; Amor, se devo piangere,* and "Dite, o pensieri miei" from the cantata *Infelice Pensier*.

27. A detailed account of the cantatas in his private collection, which became a part of the library of Geneviève Thibault after his death, was never published by Prunières. But he compiled a "Catalogue des manuscripts italienes de Cantates des XVIIe et XVIIIe Siècles de la Bibliothèque de M. Henry Prunières à Paris" which describes the manuscripts in general. There is an undated typewritten copy of this catalogue at the New York Public Library.

28. See the list of these in Geneviève Thibault's article "Henry Prunières," *MGG*, X (1962), 1667-1668.

29. The essay is published in the *Encyclopedie de la musique et dictionnaire du Conservatoire* (Paris, 1913-1939) II, 5, 3390-3410.

30. Ghislanzoni calls *Al bel lume d'un volto* on ff. 162v-164 of this manuscript "la bozza originaria" (p. 311) but he does not include all the pieces in the same hand in his catalogue.

31. See Ghislanzoni, pp. 18-19. An excellent and detailed account of this manuscript is given by Alexander Silbiger, *Italian Manuscript Sources of 17th century Keyboard Music*, UMI Research Press, 1979, pp. 86-92. The instrumental music in Add. 30491 appears

to have been copied by Rossi in Naples c. 1610-1620; the monodies by Peri and Monteverdi were probably added by Rossi after 1620 in Rome.

32. Barb. lat. 4175 is probably not earlier than 1642, if the aria *Dove mi spingi, amore* copied there was composed for *Il Palazzo Incantato* which had its first performance February 22, 1642. Barb. lat. 4201, 4204 and 4205 are undated, but were probably begun before 1638 (see M. Murata, "Pasqualini," *Analecta Musicologica*, 1976, p. 132). Barb. lat. 4221 bears the date 1638; Barb. lat. 4220, the date 1654; Barb. lat. 4219, the date 1656; Barb. lat. 4223 seems to be dated 1658 and Barb. lat. 4222 is dated 1676. These manuscripts, however, are in the hand of Marc'Antonio Pasqualini (see G. Rose, "Pasqualini as Copyist," *Analecta Musicologica*, 1974, pp. 170-175).

33. The solo pieces are in a hand that differs from that of the instrumental pieces. It appears that the volume was originally intended to include only neat and careful copies of instrumental pieces by Luigi's teacher Giovanni De Macque and by De Macque's colleagues of the Neapolitan school, for the few solo pieces at the end of the volume are interspersed on free pages between the instrumental pieces and are not mentioned in the table of contents (which was drawn up in the hand of the instrumental pieces before the monodies were added). In spite of the striking differences between the handwriting of the solo pieces and that of the instrumental compositions, Silbiger, *Italian Manuscript Sources*, p. 87, finds that the writing is in all likelihood the work of a single person.

34. Although he attributes all the music from f. 1 through f. 105 to Luigi, Ghislanzoni omits *Dove miri pensiero*, ff. 39v-45, probably by accident. It is omitted, too, in Celani's index of the manuscript. See "Canzoni musicate del secolo XVII," *RMI*, XII (1905), pp. 109-150.

35. *Dove mi spingi, amore*, attributed to Marc'Antonio Pasqualini in 1 Rc, 2467; *Non temo di morte* attributed to Marc'Antonio Pasqualini in B Br, II 3947 and in I Rc, 2467; *Occhi belli a me crudeli*, attributed to Pasqualini in B Br, II 3947; *Legate un pensiero*, attributed to Pasqualini in B Br, II 3947 and in I Rvat, Barb. lat. 4168, and *Bel volto, m'ancidi*, attributed to Marc'Antonio Pasqualini in I MOE, Mus. F. 157 and in Rc, 2467.

36. *Perche ratto così il lampo del sole* (Thematic Index I, no. 146).

37. See Alberto Cametti, "Marc'Antonio Pasqualini," *Musica d'Oggi*, Anno III (1921), n.3 pp. 69-71, and n. 4, pp. 97-99; Oscar Mischiati, "Marc'Antonio Pasqualini," *MGG*, vol. X (1962), col. 861; also Margaret Murata, "Further Remarks on Pasqualini and the Music of MAP," *Analecta*, pp. 125-145. Mischiati, following Ghislanzoni (p. 92 and p. 112, fn. 5), gives Marc'Antonio the surname "Streviglio." There is no basis at all for believing that Pasqualini was ever called by this name. For the meaning of "Streviglio," see Volume 1, p. 71. Pasqualini did have the surname "Malagigia" which Ghislanzoni mentions (p. 29), and which Cametti pointed out in the article mentioned above, p. 70.

38. Ghislanzoni, p. 279, below item 237.

39. Gloria Rose, "Pasqualini as Copyist," suggests that the inscription MAP in the Barberini manuscripts refers to Pasqualini as copyist. I am convinced, however, that wher-

ever the inscription is placed at the beginning of a composition, it names the composer. See also above, p. 5.

40. F Psg, 3372; I Bc, Q 50 and Q 48; I Rc, 2467 and 2478; I Rbn, 141; I Rvat, 4163; B Bc, II 3947; F Pthibault, Rec. H.P.5 and Il Libro di Salvator Rosa, and in other manuscripts in the Naples conservatory and in the Estense library in Modena.

41. Ghislanzoni, p. 71.

42. The sources are listed in Ghislanzoni, pp. 73-75; the aria is mentioned on p. 81. A reproduction of I Rvat, Chigi Q V 51 was published by Garland Publishers, New York, 1977 with an introduction by Howard Mayer Brown.

43. Stuart Reiner, "Collaboration in *La Catena d'Adone*," paper read to the American Musicological Society, Washington, D.C., December 27, 1964.

44. Jander thesis, cited in note 4, above, chapter 5.

45. For arias from Luigi's operas identified in cantata manuscripts, see Appendix. I have also been able to identify seventeen pieces, most of them anonymous, in the Bologna MS Q 47, as arias from Marco Marazzoli's *La Vita Humana* of 1658; *O morte gradita* in the Casanatense MS 2472, as an aria from Stefano Landi's *S. Alessio*; and *Se perfido amore*, anonymous in the Luneburg MS K.N.145 Welter S. 23, as a duet from Cesti's *La Dori*. Also, *Se l'anima mia*, anonymous in the MS B 2560 at the Florence Conservatory, was probably sung at one of the performances of Cesti's *Orontea*.

46. Enrico Celani, "Canzoni musicate del secolo XVII," op. cit. This bibliographical study is full of omissions and should not be relied on. Although Ghislanzoni discovered some of the pieces overlooked by Celani, his corrections are not systematic and are evident only to those who know both the Celani lists and the manuscripts.

47. David Burrows, "The Cantatas of Antonio Cesti," p. 100, is of this opinion.

48. Gloria Rose, "Pasqualini as Copyist," p. 173, and Margaret Murata, "Further Remarks on Pasqualini," p. 132, fn. 35, both suggest that the miscellanies Barb. lat. 4201, 4204, and 4205, are composing books of Luigi, and that except for the concordances with the Pasqualini cantatas in Barb. lat. 4219, 4220, 4221, 4222 and 4223, their contents are Luigi's compositions. However, with the exception of *Al bel lume*, I have found no concordances that support this suggestion. Without solid bibliographical evidence I cannot include the contents of these three manuscripts among Luigi's oeuvre.

49. *Al bel lume* is mentioned above. *Lasciate ch'io peni*, anon. in Barb. lat. 4219, is attributed to Luigi in I Rvat, Chigi Q IV 16, a highly reliable source. According to Ghislanzoni, pp. 112-115, this piece forms part of "una specia di ampia cantata quasi oratorio" *Il Peccator Pentito*. *Dove mi spingi, amore*, which appears in Barb. lat. 4223 with the inscription "MAP Poesia di N.N. AB," is found in the scores of Luigi's opera *Il Palazzo Incantato*.

50. Only six of Luigi's compositions were published during his lifetime (see Thematic Index 1, nos. 2, 34, 62, 92 and 94, published in 1640, and nos. 78 and 223, published in

1646). Not long after his death, in 1656, a collection of Italian solo songs, duets, and trios was published by Van Geertsom in Rotterdam. The collection begins with five anonymous solo arias, two of which are from Luigi's *Orfeo*, two others are attributed to Luigi in contemporary manuscripts, and the fifth is also attributed to Luigi in one manuscript source—though in many more Carissimi is named the composer. In 1679 two more cantatas attributed to Luigi Rossi were published in London. These two (Thematic Index 1, nos. 40 and 127) and those first four which had been published in 1640 are not extant in manuscripts of the time.

51. It appears to me that the table of contents in each of the manuscripts just listed is also in the hand of the attribution, not in the hand of any one of the copyists.

52. "Autographe Marco Marazzolis in der Biblioteca Vaticana," *Analecta Musicologica*, vii (1968), 36-66 and ix (1970), 203-294.

53. In many manuscripts the practice of coloration is continued, the blackened whole and half notes primarily indicating a momentary shift from triple to duple meter, a shift of accent.

54. Friedrich Wilhelm Riedel, "Notation D. Abendländische Musik," *MGG*, IX (Kassel, 1961), col. 1659.

55. The incipits nos. 168, 324, 341, 365, 372, 381, 383, 402 and 429, with accidentals repeated within the measure, prove the general practice.

56. See incipits nos. 84, 107, 155, 185, 191, 337, and 390.

57. Incipits nos. 38, 137, 157, 225, 242, 245, 297, 317, and 415.

58. A phenomenon that occurs exceptionally in I Bc, Q 46 and Q 50; Fc, D 2357, and more frequently in MOe, Mus. G 239 and GB Lbm, Add. 30491, and regularly in I Rbn, 56.

59. If the chromatic step, however, is implied in the realization of the continuo part, it is often not provided in the bass figuration, but must be inferred from the musical context.

60. See incipits nos. 81, 100, 214, 223, and 367.

61. See incipits nos. 58, 93, 126, 191, 200, 237, 390 and 417.

62. See incipits nos. 41, 157, 263, 297, 362, and 391.

63. See the incipit of *La bella*, no. 103.

64. It still retained this function, as the following passage in *Ars Cantandi* demonstrates: "Das weiche Gesang wird erkennet wann gleich zu Anfang nach dem gezeichneten Schlussel das runde b verzeichnet stehet." Giovan Giacomo Carissimi, *Ars Cantandi* . . . (Augsburg, 1693 and 1696), p. 4. Facsimiles of the 1696 edition at the Library of Congress are in James R. Douglas (translator), "The Art of Singing. A Translation in English of *Ars Cantandi*," unpublished Master's thesis (Union Theological Seminary, 1949). The translator has consistently and erroneously translated *"harte Gesang"* as

"major key" rather than *hexachordum durum*, and *"weiche Gesang"* as "minor key" rather than *hexachordum molle*.

65. Gustave Reese, *Music in the Renaissance* (New York, 1954), pp. 45-47.

66. About one hundred and seventy of the cantatas listed in this catalogue have a signature of one flat.

67. See *Difenditi, amore*, ex. III, fifth measure from the close; *Taci, ohimè*, ex. XVI, measures 24, 25, 27 and 37; *Non m'affligete*, ex. XXV, measure 65.

68. *Ho voto di non amare*, 93.

69. See *Giusto così*, 81, where the second phrase begins with the opening melodic figure, and compare the end of measure 2 of *Ciglia brune*, 414, with the end of measure 1.

70. See incipits nos. 100, 107, 367, 391 and 414.

71. Incipits nos. 103 and 263.

72. Incipits nos. 100, 223, 367, and 376.

73. Compare the incipits *V'è, v'è*, 201 and *Sovra un sasso*, 386, to the opening of *Su la sponda*, 391, and the incipits of *Horche in notturno*, 274, and *Anime, voi*, 18, to the opening of *Taci, ohimè*, 191.

Thematic Index 1

Cantatas Attributed to Luigi Rossi on Reliable Grounds

1. A chi, lasso, crederò? Voi, begl'occhi. Wo. 1, Gh. 1, Re. 21.

F Pn, Vm7 6, f. 12, Luigi Rossi.
D SW, 4718a, pp. 35-36, Luigi (lacks text of 2d strophe).
GB Och, 350, pp. 42-43, anon.
GB Och, 17, f. 12, anon (in a minor).
GB Lbm, Harl. 7549, f. 11, anon. (soprano part only, and incomplete).
B Bc, 17197, pp. 10-11 (copy of 4718a).

GB Lbm, G 82(2), *Select Ayres and Dialogues to Sing to the Theorbo-Lute or Basse-Viol* . . . The Second Book (London: William Godbid for John Playford, 1669), p. 99, anon. Wotquenne describes the state of *A chi lasso* here as "très disfiguré." The same description fits the version in Harl. 7549, a MS which also contains other pieces found in Playford collections. It may be a source of the printed pieces or a copy of them.

2.   Acuto gelo, tu che mordace. Wo. 2, Gh. 2, Re. 49.

I Rvat and Rsc, *Raccolta d'arie spirituali* . . . (Roma: Vincenzo Bianchi, 1640), p. 16, Luigi de Rossi.
B BC, 17193, p. 95 (a copy of the print).

3.   Adagio, speranze, al suono pietoso. Wo. 3, Gh. 3.

F Pn, Vm7 6, f. 16v, Luigi Rossi.
B Bc, 15261, pp. 5-6 (copy of Vm7 6).

Jules Ecorcheville, *Catalogue du Fonds de Musique Ancienne* . . . (Paris, 1910-1914), VII, 187, incorrectly gives the incipit *Speranze al suono pietoso*.

4.   Addio, addio, perfida, addio. Wo. 4, Gh. 4, Re. 14.

D SW, 4718a, p. 4 and pp. 12-13, Luigi.
B Bc, 17197, pp. 7-9 (copy of 4718a).

5.   Adorate mie catene, per pietà siate men dure. Wo. 5, Gh. 5, Re. 22.

GB Ckc, MS 22, ff. 182-183, Luigi Rossi.
F Pn, Vm7 6, f. 17v, Luigi Rossi.
GB Och, 947, ff. 113-116, luigi (attribution is not in the hand of the text).
D Kl, 2° Mus. 34, ff. 82-83, anon. (lacks text of 3d strophe).
I Fbn, Magl. XIX.26, ff. 19-21, anon. (The text is somewhat varied; it
    begins "Adorate mie catene, deh, d'afliggermi lasciate.")
B Bc, 17197, pp. 127-128 (copy of 2° Mus. 34).

6.   A la rota, a la benda, al biondo crine. Wo. 7, Gh. 9, Re. 1.

I Rc, 2477, ff. 197-216, Luigi (has the title "La Fortuna").
F Pthibault, GT 3, ff. 11-36v, Luigi Rossi.
GB Lbm, Harl. 1265, ff. 37-62v, Luigi Rossi (has the title "La Fortuna")
B Bc, 17193, pp. 107-121 (copy of Harl. 1265).

Wotquenne and Ghislanzoni suggest that the words "Del britannico Re
l'infausto caso" refer to the decapitation of Charles I of England in January, 1649. The author is unknown. However, both Lady Morgan and
Ghislanzoni assume that the text is Salvator Rosa's. Lady Morgan simply
says, "The words of the canzonette beginning 'Or che la notte del silenzio
amica' and of another called *La Fortuna*, are supposed to have been
written by Salvator Rosa."[1] Ghislanzoni argues that the author may be
Rosa because the latter had returned to Rome in 1649 and had no doubt
read a pamphlet published in Macerata concerning the execution of
Charles I. And supposing Rosa a friend of Luigi, Ghislanzoni believes
that the two collaborated in Rome after Luigi's return from Paris late in

1649 or early in 1650. Limentani erroneously believing that both pieces
were composed before 1640 (only the former was cited by Della Valle in
1640; see below, no. 87) says Rosa is not the author because he could not
have known Luigi before 1640.[2] But if the reference in the text is to the
decapitation of Charles I in 1649, *La Fortuna* was not composed before
1640 and Rosa may be its author, though there is no conclusive evidence
that he is.

7. Al cenno d'una speranza dal petto il cor si partì. Wo. 6, Gh. 8,
    Re. 50.

B Br, II 3947, ff. 113-115v, Luigi Rossi.
I Rvat, Q IV 5, ff. 77-78, anon.
F Pa, M.948, ff. 17-18v, anon.
    (closes with a ritornello marked "Chiaccona").
F Pc, Res. 2096, pp. 64-65, anon. (lacks continuo).
B Bc, 17193, pp. 38-40 (copy of II 3947).
Eins, 87, 24 (copy of II 3947).

8. All'hor ch'il ben dal male non discernevi.

I Bc, V/289, ff. 209-210v, Luigi Rossi, text by Monsig:re Vai.

9. All'hor ch'il forte Alcide nel gran campo di Marte. Wo. 9, Gh. 12, Re. 76.

F Pn. Rés, Vm7 102, ff. 87-90v, Luigi Rossi.
(The author of the text is not named. But in the index the text of the piece immediately above this one is attributed to Domenico Benigni, which may account for Ghislanzoni's error in attributing the text of *All'hor ch'il forte Alcide* to the same author.)
B Bc 17192, pp. 132-143 (copy of Rés. Vm7 102).

10. All'ombra d'una speranza mi posi a dormire un di. Wo. 8, Gh. 11, Re. 24.

GB Lbm, Harl. 1501, ff. 34r-34v, Luiggi Rossi.
I Rc, 2505, ff. 122-123, anon.
B Bc, 17197, pp. 119-120 (copy of Harl. 1501).

11. Al soave spirar d'aure serene. Wo. 10, Gh. 13, Re. 75.

I Rvat, Chigi Q VII 99, ff. 1-6v, Luige Rossi, text by Em[inentissi]mo Rospigliosi.

F Pn, Rés. Vm7 59, ff. 1-8v, Luigi Rossi, text by Monsignore Rospigliosi.

GB Lbm, Harl. 1265, ff. 125-142, Luigi Rossi.

I Rc, 2477, ff. 13-22v, Luigi Rossi (the attribution is not in the hand of the text).

I Rvat, Chigi Q IV 3, ff. 39v-51v, anon.

I Nc, 33.5.18, ff. 59-70v, anon. (the attribution Bassi is a later addition).

I Nc, 33.3.11, ff. 85-92, anon.

I Rc, 2505, ff. 2-10, anon.

12.   Amanti, piangete a miei pianti. Wo. 11, Gh. 14, Re. 15.

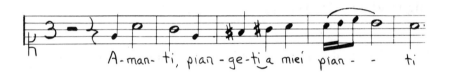

I Nc, 33.4.12, ff. 161v-166v, Luigi Rossi.

I Nc, 33.4.7, ff. 83-88v, Luigi Rossi.

GB Lbm, Harl. 1273, f. 78, Luigi Rossi (lacks text of 2d strophe).

D SW, 4718a, pp. 43-45, Luigi (lacks text of 2d strophe).

GB Och, 951, ff. 25-28v, Luigi (the attribution is not in the hand of the text).

B Bc, 17193, pp. 163-164 (copy of Harl. 1273).

13.   A me stesso il pensier mio talhor parla. Wo. 12, Gh. 15, Re. 23.

F Pn, Vm7 6, ff. 9-9v, Luigi Rossi.

B Br, II 3947, ff. 83-84v, Luigi Rossi.

B Bc, F 664, pp. 31-33; XY 8286, p. 88; 28072, pp. 30-31 (copies of II 3947).

Eins, 87, 18 (copy of II 3947).

Another setting for soprano solo:
F Pthibault, Rec. H.P. 31, pp. 113-115, anon.

14.   Amor così si fà, così si premia chi per te pena? Wo. 13, Gh. 18,
      Re. 51.

I Rvat, Barb. lat. 4163, ff. 37-38v, Luigi.
B Bc, 17197, pp. 156-157 (copy of 4163).

15.   Amor e perche con pianti e sospiri. Wo. 14, Gh. 19, Re. 25.

GB Ouf, MS U.210.4, ff. 39-42, Luigi Rossi (incipit 2).
F Pn, Vm7 17, p. 71, Luigi (incipit 2).
F Pn, Vm7 3, ff. 27v-29, anon (incipit 1).
B Bc, F 664, pp. 29-30, 28072 pp. 28-29 (copies of Vm7 17).

16.   Amor giura che m'aiuta proponendo stravaganze. Wo. 15, Gh. 20.

F Pn, Vm7 6, f. 12v, Luigi Rossi.
B Bc, 15261, pp. 20-21 (copy of Vm7 6).

17.   Amor, s'io mi querelo d'amar beltà superba. Wo. 16, Gh. 22, Re. 62.

I Rc, 2467, ff. 48v-53, Luigi.
F Pn, Vm7 6, f. 6, Louigi Rossi.
GB Lbm, Harl. 1501, ff. 58v-59, Luiggi Rossi (the meter is ³⁄₄).
I Rvat, 4175, ff. 59v-63, anon.
B Bc, 17197, pp. 135-137 (copy of Harl. 1501).

18.   Anime, voi che sete dalle furie. Wo. 18, Gh. 24, Re. 2.

GB Ouf, MS U.210.4, ff. 49-56v, Luigi Rossi.
B Br, II 3947, ff. 1-8v, Luigi Rossi.
F Pthibault Libro di Salvator: Rosa, no. 12, Luigi.
GB Och, 350, pp. 84-89, Luigi Rossi.

I Rvat, Chigi Q VII 99, ff. 61v-64 Luige Rossi.

I Rsc, G 885, ff. 23-28, del d° (Luigi Rossi).

F Pn Vm7 6, ff. 8-8v, Luigi Rossi.

F Pn Vm7 17, pp. 59-67 Luigi.

GB Cfm, 24 F 4, ff. 100-101, Luigi Rossi.

GB Och, 950, ff. 53-60, luigi (the attribution is not in the hand of the text).

I Rvat, Barb. lat. 4150, 83-88 anon.

US CHH, Music Vault M2. 1 M1, ff. 164v-167v, anon.

I Rc, 2482, ff. 17-22v (old foliation), anon.

GB Lbm, Harl. 1863, ff. 150v-153, anon.

GB Lbm, Harl. 1264, ff. 11v-17, anon.

D SW, 4718a, pp. 8-11, anon.

I Nc, 33.4.17, II, 75-78, Carlo Caprioli.

B Bc, 17193, pp. 14-19 (copy of II 3947).

Eins, 87, 1-2 (copy of II 3947).

19. A qual dardo il cor si deve, forse a quel che vibra amore? Wo. 20, Gh. 26.

I Bc, V/289, ff. 157-162v, Luigi Rossi, text by Dom. Benigni.

F Pn, Rés. Vm7 102, ff. 79-82v, Luigi Rossi, text by Domenico Benigni.

F Pn, Vm7 6, ff. 11v-12, Luigi Rossi.

US CA, MS Mus 106, no. 11, ff. (41-44v), anon.

B Bc, 17192, pp. 162-177 (copy of Rés. Vm7 102).

20.   Armatevi di sdegno, offesi amanti. Gh. 28.

I Rvat, Chigi Q VI 85, ff. 50v-52, Luigi (lacks text of the second half of the aria).

The anonymous piece in Barb. lat. 4204, ff. 118-120, which Ghislanzoni cites as a concordance, is neither the same music nor the same text. The duet Ghislanzoni describes (catalogue, no. 272) as an elaboration of *Armatevi di sdegno* is not related to it either but is a concordance of the piece in 4204. (See below, no. 411)
(The date on the MS seems to be 1644, not 1641 as Ghislanzoni and Cametti report.)[3]

21.   Armatevi d'orgoglio, luci belle, a che tardate? Wo. 21, Gh. 29.

F Pn, Vm7 6, f. 5, Luigi Rossi.
I Rc, 2475, ff. 43-46v, anon.
B Bc, 15261, pp. 15-17 (copy of Vm7 6).

22.   A tanti sospiri, a lagrime tante, agl'aspri martiri. Wo. 22, Gh. 30.

I Rc, 2466, ff. 183-184v, Luigi de Rossi.
B Bc, 11008, pp. 76-77 (copy of 2466).

23.   Atra notte il velo ombroso distendea sovra i mortali. Wo. 23, Gh. 31.

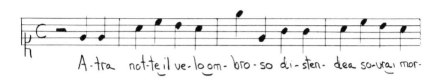

F Pn, Vm7 6, f. 5v, Luigi Rossi.
US CA, MS Mus 106, no. 41, ff. (125-126v), anon.
US SFdeBellis, MS Misc.V.LXIX, ff. 74-79v, anon.
B Bc, 15261, pp. 17-19 (copy of Vm7 6).

Another setting for soprano solo:
D Kl, ms.2.Mus.34, ff. 59v-61, Ziani.
GB Lbm, *Canzonette a voce sola di Pietro Andrea Ziani, Opera Ottava*
    (Venice, 1670), f. 85.
A third setting for soprano solo:
I Nc, 33.4.13, II, ff. 97-108v, Tonno (Antonio) Solino.

24.   Begl'occhi, che dite? Volete che mora. Wo. 25, Gh. 34, Re. 26.

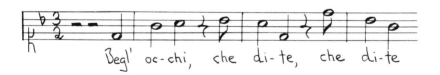

F Pn, Vm7 17, pp. 74-78, Luigi (lacks text of 2d strophe).
I Nc, 33.4.14, ff. 111-116, anon.
GB Ouf, MS U.210.4, ff. 19-22v, anon.
B Bc, F 664, pp. 51-54; 28072, pp. 51-54 (copies of Vm7 17).

25.   Begl'occhi, pietà! son vinto, vi cedo. Wo. 26, Gh. 35.

F Pn, Vm7 6, f. 13, Luigi Rossi.
B Bc, 15261, pp. 34-35 (copy of Vm7 6).

Another setting for soprano solo (see below, no. 304):
I Rvat, Barb. lat. 4200, ff. 63-65, anon.

26.   Benche roca pur impetra poche note al mesto core. Wo. 27, Gh. 39.

I G1, A-5-Cass, ff. 66-69v, Luigi.
F Pn, Vm7 6, f. 14, Luigi Rossi.
I Rvat, Barb. lat. 4150, ff. 43-45v, anon.
B Bc, 15261, pp. 59-61 (copy of Vm7 6).

27.   Che cosa mi dite? Che si cangino i contenti. Wo. 28, Gh. 43.

F Pn, Vm7 6, ff. 7v-8, Luigi Rossi.
B Bc, 15261, pp. 73-75 (copy of Vm7 6).

28. Che dici, mio core? Beltà peregrina entrar vuol. Wo. 29, Gh. 44.

F Pn, Vm7 6, f. 13v, Luigi Rossi.
B Bc, 15261, pp. 1-2 (copy of Vm7 6).

29. Che farò, m'innamoro, sì o nò? Wo. 30, Gh. 45, Re. 27.

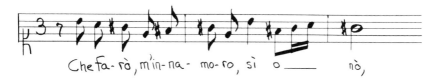

I Bc, V/289, ff. 207-208v, Luigi Rossi, text by Monsignore Vai.
F Pn, Vm7 6, f. 3, Luigi Rossi.
GB Lbm, Harl. 1863, ff. 113v-115, Luiggi. (lacks texts of 2d and 3d
    strophes).
F Pc, Rés. 2096, pp. 44-47, anon. (lacks continuo).
I Rvat, Barb. lat. 4150, ff. 71v-74, then skip back to ff. 63-63v, anon.
I Nc, 33.5.18, ff. 54-55v, anon.
US CA, MS Mus 106, no. 35, ff. (119-120v), anon.

The analysis given by Ghislanzoni is based on the version in Harl. 1863
where a da capo rubric is mistakenly placed after the fifth verse of the
first strophe, making the sixth verse appear as the beginning of a new
strophe. The actual second strophe, as well as the third, is missing. In
the other MSS the da capo rubric does not occur until the entire first
strophe is completed. Texts are given for strophes 2 and 3; in MS 4150
the music is written out for all three strophes.

30.   Che sventura! Son tant'anni ch'io vi servo. Wo. 31, Gh. 46.

GB Cke, MS 22, ff. 183v-184, Luigi Rossi.
I Nc, 33.4.12, ff. 127-130, Luigi Rossi.
I Rc, 2466, ff. 139-142, Luigi.
F Pn, Vm7 6, f. 14v, Luigi Rossi.
F Pthibault, G.T.3, ff. 75-78v, Luigi Rossi.
GB Och, 949, ff. 81-84, Luigi.
I Rc, 2475, ff. 111-113v, anon.
La, pp. 36-39 (the sources are MSS 2466 and 2475).

31.   Che tardi più, che tardi per le piagge.

F Pc, Rés. 2096, pp. 9r-103, Luigi Rossi (lacks continuo).

32.   Che vuoi più da me, fierissimo amore? Wo. 33, Gh. 49.

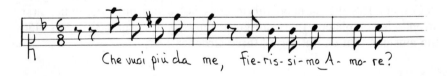

F Pn, Vm7 6, f. 13, Luigi Rossi.
B Bc, 15261, pp. 32-33 (copy of Vm7 6).

33. Chi batte il mio core, chi e? L'occhiuto sospetto.

I Rc, 2467, ff. 19v-32, Luigi, text by Melosi.
I Rvat, Chigi Q IV 8, ff. 7v-14v, anon.
I Rc, 2482, ff. 29-36v, anon.
I Ria, MS. 1, ff. 23-32 (since folio 23 is missing, the folios are 24-33), anon. (lacks the first 17 measures).

Another setting for soprano solo:
I MOe, Mus.F 1533, anon.
A third setting for soprano solo:
F Pc, D.11837, f. 75 ff., anon.

34. Chi cercando và le pene le dimand'all'alma mia. Wo. 34, Gh. 50.

F Pn, Vm7 6, f. 15v, Luigi Rossi.
I Nc, 33.4.19, II, 1-2v, anon. (the attribution Pasqualini is a later addition).
B Bc, 15261, pp. 49-50 (copy of Vm7 6). The meter indicated here is ³/4, but many of the measures are noted in ³/2.

35. Chi consiglia un dubbio, core, che nel seno.

GB Ouf, MS U.210.4, ff. 92-95v, Luigi Rossi.
US SFdeBellis, MS Misc.V.LXVIII, ff. 49v-53v, anon.

36.   Chi desia di salire al monte di virtù. Wo. 35, Gh. 51, Re. 53.

I Rvat and Rsc, *Raccolta d'arie spirituali* . . . (Roma: Vincenzo Bianchi,
   1640), p. 20, Luigi de Rossi.
B Bc, 17193, p. 101 (copy of the print).

37.   Chi di voi nova mi da d'un pensier. Wo. 36, Gh. 52.

F Pn, Vm7 6, f. 8v, Luigi Rossi.
B Bc, 15261, pp. 55-56 (copy of Vm7 6).

Another setting of the text for solo voice:
I Rvat, Chigi Q IV 8, ff. 73-74v, anon.

38.   Chi mi credeva instabile pria di me si cangiò. Wo. 37, Gh. 53, Re. 77.

GB Lbm, Harl. 1501, ff. 36v-38v, Luiggi Rossi.
GB Och, 17, ff. 18-19, anon.
B Bc, 17197, pp. 121-126 (copy of Harl. 1501).

The melody of the first strophe is not repeated for the second and third strophes, as Ghislanzoni says it is, but is varied for each strophe.

39.   Chi non ha speranza alcuna che lusinghi il suo pensiero. Wo. 38, Gh. 54.

I Rc, 2477, ff. 23-28v, Luigi Rossi.
F Pn, Vm7 6, ff. 16-16v, Luigi Rossi.
I Rvat, Barb. lat. 4208, ff. 44v-46, anon.
B Bc, 15261, pp. 78-79 (copy of Vm7 6).

40.   Chi non sa fingere, goder non sa. Wo. 39, Gh. 55.

I Rvat, US NYp, GB Lbm, *Scelta di Canzonette* . . . (London: A. Godbid & J. Playford, 1679), pp. 64-65, Luigi Rossi.
B Bc, 17196, p. 29 (copy of the print).

41.   Ch'io sospiri al vostro foco, ch'io languisca. Wo. 40, Gh. 56, Re. 52.

F Pn, Res. Vm7 59, ff. 125-126v, Luigi Rossi, text by Domenico Benigni
(in c minor).
I Fbn, Magl. XIX 26, ff. 29-30v, anon. (lacks text of 3d strophe).
I Rvat, Barb. lat. 4374, pp. 17-18, anon. (for tenor; in c minor).
B Bc, 17192, pp. 170-173 (copy of Rés. Vm7 59).

42.   Ch'io speri o disperi, amor, che ti fa? Wo. 41, Gh. 57, Re. 28.

I G1, A-5-Cass., ff. 153-159, Luigi.
B Br, II 3947, ff. 63-66v, Luigi Rossi.
I Rvat, Barb. lat. 4146, ff. 57v-61, anon.
I Rc, 2226, ff. 26v-28, anon. (in B-flat).
I Rvat, Barb. lat. 4374, pp. 175-180, anon. (for tenor).
B Bc, 17193, pp. 43-46 (copy of II 3947).
Eins, 87, 14 (copy of II 3947).

Another version for soprano solo:
I Rbn, 71.9.A.33, ff. 55-58v, Ca[rissi]mi.
Yet another version for soprano:
F Pc, Res. 2096, pp. 150-152, anon. (lacks continuo and text of 3d strophe).

43.   Chi trovasse una speranza che da me lungi sen' và. Wo. 42, Gh. 58.

F Pn, Vm7 6, ff. 7-7v, Luigi Rossi.
I Ria, MS. 1, ff. 4-6v, anon.
B Bc, 15261, pp. 75-77 (copy of Vm7 6).

44.   Come è breve il gioir d'un miser core. Wo. 43, Gh. 61.

F Pn, Vm7 6, ff. 10-11, Luigi Rossi.
B Bc, 15261, pp. 71-73 (copy of Vm7 6).

Another setting, for two sopranos and continuo:
I Nc, 60.1.50, ff. 47-69v, anon. (follows a composition by Carissimi and
   precedes one by Luigi).

45.   Come penare, non l'intendo. Wo. 44, Gh. 62.

I Rc, 2466, ff. 113-116v, Luigi.
F Pn, Vm7 6, f. 13v, Luigi Rossi.
B Bc, 15261, pp. 25-27 (copy of Vm7 6; lacks 5th verse of the 2d strophe).

46.   Come tosto sparisce beltà caduce e frale.

I Rc, 2472, pp. 39-40, Luigi Rossi.

47.   Con amor e senza spene un bel niente mi mantiene. Gh. 388.

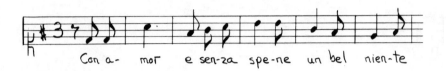

I G1, A-5 Cass., ff. 83-90, Luigi.
I Nc, 33.4.19, II, 5-7, anon.

48.   Con amor si pugna invano cinto il cor di smalto duro. Gh. 63.

I Rc, 2466, ff. 109-112, Luigi.
I Rvat, Barb. lat. 4208, ff. 66v-69v, anon.
I Nc, 33.4.15, I, 89-92, anon. (the attribution Tenaglia is a later addition).

49.   Con occhi belli e fieri colmi d'amore e d'ira. Wo. 46, Gh. 65, Re. 78.

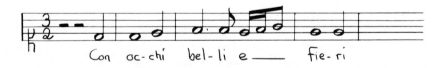

I Rc, 2483, ff. 50-67v, Luigi Rossi.
F Pn, Rés. Vm7 59, ff. 9-16v, Luigi Rossi, text by Fabio della Corgna.
I Rc, 2505, ff. 10v-18v, anon.
B Bc, F 664, pp. 71-85 (copy of Rés. Vm7 59).
B Bc, 28072, pp. 72-87 (copy made in 1910).

50. Con voi parlo amanti. Chiedete ad amore. Wo. 48, Gh. 67.

F Pn, Vm7 6, f. 15, Luigi Rossi.
B Bc, 15261, pp. 40-42 (copy of Vm7 6).
   In 15261 the opening words are "Con voi parto;" when the refrain returns, however, the words are correctly copied "con voi parlo." The incipit given in both previous catalogues is incorrect.
Another setting for soprano solo:
I Rsc, G885, ff. 111-114v, Carlo del Viol°.

51. Così và, dice il mio core, in amore chi più serve. Gh. 68, Re. 29.

I Nc, 33.4.12, ff. 109-114v, Luigi Rossi.
F Pn, Vm7 6, ff. 15v-16, Luigi Rossi.
I Rvat, Barb. lat. 4208, ff. 62v-66, anon.
B Bc, 17197, pp. 162-164 (copy of 33.4.12).
P, pp. 15-18.

52. Da perfida speranza un alma lusingata. Wo. 89, Gh. 129, Re. 6.

I Rc, 2468, ff. 97-108, Luigi Rossi.
GB Lbm, Harl. 1265, ff. 153-166v, Luigi Rossi (has the title *Il Disperato*).

GB Och, 946, ff. 53-60v, luigi (the attribution is not in the hand of the text).

I Fbn, Magl. XIX 26, ff. 31-38v, anon.

I PAc, CF-111-1, ff. 135-140, anon.

F Pthibault, Rec.H.P.8, ff. 58v-67, anon.

I Vc, Busta 16-48-N.47, Carissimi.

I Busseto, Villa Verdi, two unclassified manuscripts. In the MS dated 1689 the cantata is in its most complete form and is attributed to Sig. Rossi; in the second MS, ff. 79v-85, anon., the version of the cantata is like that in Magl. XIX 26.

B Bc, 17197, pp. 103-113 (copy of Harl. 1265).

In all of the sources except Och, 946, the first word is "Da"; the incipit given in the previous catalogues begins "La" as does Och, 946. Magl. XIX 26 lacks the 2d strophe and the 2d recitative; Vc, N.47 lacks the arioso ending. Both MSS lack the final "Sarabanda," six measures to be played by the continuo.

53.   Degg'io dunque in amore esser sempre tradito? Wo. 50, Gh. 72.

F Pn, Vm7 6, f. 4v, Luigi Rossi (lacks text of 2d strophe).

I Rvat, Barb. lat. 4175, ff. 69v-73, anon.

B Bc, 15261, pp. 80-82 (copy of Vm7 6).

54.   Deh, soccorri ad un che more. Wo. 51, Gh. 73.

F Pn, Vm7 6, f. 5, Luigi Rossi.

B Bc, 15261. pp. 57-58 (copy of Vm7 6).

55.   Deh, soffri, mio core, con fronte sicura. Wo. 52, Gh. 74, Re. 64.

D SW, 4718a, pp. 122-123, Luigi (lacks text of 2d strophe).
F Pn, Vm7 6, f. 4, anon.
B Bc, 17197, p. 21 (copy of 4718a).
B Br, *Canzonette amorose* . . . (Rotterdam: Giovanni Van Geertsom, 1656).
    Basso Continuo part book, p. 4, anon.

56.   De la vita in sù l'aurora lagrimando.

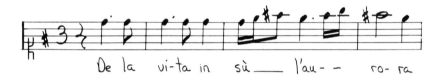

I Rsc, G 885, ff. 11-22v, del d° (Luigi Rossi).

57.   Difendi, mio core, l'entrata a l'amore.

I Rc, 2479, ff. 197v-199v, Louigi R.

58.   Difenditi, amore! Per foco di sdegno. Wo. 54, Gh. 77, Re. 31.

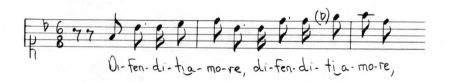

I Bc, V/289, ff. 197-199v, Luigi Rossi, text by Domenico Benigni.
F Pn, Rés. Vm7 59, ff. 119-120v, Luigi Rossi, text by Domenico Benigni.
I Vnm, It.IV.742 (=10318), ff. 3v-6, Luigi Rossi, 1646 (lacks text of 2d
    and 3d strophes).
I Vnm, It.IV.743 (=10317), ff. 44v-51, anon.
I Rvat, Barb. lat., 4175, ff. 65v-69, anon.
F Pa, M 948, ff. 67-68v, anon.
B Bc, 17192, pp. 174-177 (copy of Rés. Vm7 59).
Re, II, 2, 381-383.

59.   Difenditi, o core! Per lampo fugace. Wo. 55, Gh. 78.

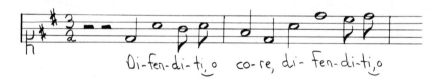

GB Lbm, Harl. 1501, ff. 12-13, Luiggi Rossi.
B Bc, 17197, pp. 133-135; 15258, pp. 19-20 (copies of Harl. 1501).

The refrain of this piece and that of *Difenditi, amore! Per foco*, no. 58
above, are identical in their structure: the number of verses, the meter,
the rhyme-scheme, and even the first word of the corresponding verses
being the same. In fact, Luigi seems to have composed two settings of
the same poem using variant refrains for the text of the first strophe
following the refrain *Difenditi, amore!* is the same as the text that follows
Difenditi, o core! The second and third strophes that follow *Difenditi,
amore!* are, however, omitted after *Difenditi, o core!* (See Volume 1, pp.
52-53.)

60.   Disperati, che aspetti più, abbandonato core? Wo. 57, Gh. 79.

F Pn, Vm7 6, ff. 3v-4, Luigi Rossi.
B Bc, 15261, pp. 36-37 (copy of Vm7 6).

61.   Dissi un giorno ad amore: io sono amante. Wo. 56, Gh. 81.

F Pn, Vm7 6, f. 3v, Luigi Rossi.
I Rc, 2475, ff. 91-92v, anon.
B Bc, 15261, pp. 53-54 (copy of Vm7 6).

62.   Diva, tu che in trono assisa. Wo. 58, Gh. 82, Re. 16.

I Rvat and Rsc, *Raccolta d'arie spirituali* . . . (Roma: Vincenzo Bianchi,
     1640), pp. 3-4, Luigi de Rossi.
B Bc, 17193, p. 92 (copy of the print).
P, pp. 7-9; Su, no. 53.

63.   Dopo lungo penare tornato in libertà. Wo. 58, Gh. 83, Re. 79.

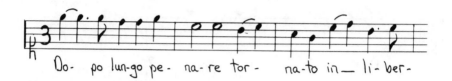

F Pn, Rés. Vm7 102, ff. 83-84v, Luigi Rossi, text by Domenico Benigni.
B Bc, F 664, pp. 47-50; 28072, pp. 47-50 (copies of Rés. Vm7 102).

64.   Dove, dove più giro fra queste piante addolorato il piede?

I Rc, 2468, ff. 27-38v, Luigi.
I Rsc, G 885, ff. 10-10v. Since folios 1-9v are missing, only the final 21
   measures of the piece are left. The attribution on the first folio must
   have been Luigi Rossi for concordances prove that "Del d°" at the
   beginning of each of the 11 consecutive pieces following *Dove, dove
   più giro* refers to Luigi.

65.   D'una bella infedele ch'ha di spirto. Wo. 50, Gh. 84, Re. 63.

GB Lbm, Harl. 1273, f. 78v, Luigi Rossi.
D SW, 4718a, pp. 46-48, Luigi (begins "Una bella").
GB Och, 17, f. 10, anon. (the voice part is written on the treble staff).
B Bc, 17197, pp. 11-13 (copy of 4718a).

GB Lbm, Add. 14336, ff. 7-8v, anon. (an arrangement for two sopranos, bass, and continuo; the two upper voices are written on treble staves).

66. E che cantar poss'io d'allegro, di bizzarro e stravagante? Wo. 61, Gh. 85.

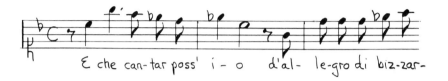

GB Och, 949, ff. 49-54 Luigi.

67. E chi non v'ameria, pupilluccie amorose. Wo. 62, Gh. 88, Re. 32.

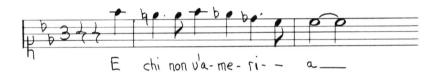

GB Lbm, Harl. 1265, ff. 91-94v, Luige.
B Bc, 17193, pp. 167-170 (copy of Harl. 1265).

Wotquenne and Ghislanzoni give a third source:
GB Lbm, Harl. 1272 (the number 1372 which appears in their catalogues is a typographical error), ff. 95v ff., anon. The cantata for tenor solo in this MS is a setting of a shortened version of the same text. The music is not like that attributed to Luige in Harl. 1265.

68. E d'amore foll'inganno che non stringan le catene.

I Rsc, G885, ff. 37-40, del dº (Luigi Rossi).

69.   E può soffrirsi amore quel che soffrendo stò? Wo. 63, Gh. 89, Re. 65.

GB Lbm, Harl. 1265, ff. 87-90, Luigi.
B Bc, 17193, pp. 171-173; 17197, pp. 100-102 (copies of Harl. 1265).

70.   Erminia sventurata, ove t'aggiri? Wo. 64, Gh. 91, Re. 80.

I Rc, 2478, ff. 4-11v (old foliation) or 1-8v (new foliation), Luigi Rossi.
I Nc, 33.4.12, ff. 75-84, Luigi Rossi.
GB Lbm, Harl. 1265, ff. 143-152v, Luigi Rossi.
I Rvat, Barb. lat. 4200, ff. 67v-72, anon.
GB Och, 946, ff. 91-96v. Carissimi (the attribution is not in the hand of the text).
B Bc, 17193, pp. 155-161 (copy of Harl. 1265).

71.   E si crede ch'io no'l sò. Wo. 65, Gh. 92.

I Rc, 2477, ff. 137-140v, Luigi Rossi (lacks text of 2d strophe).

GB Och, 951, ff. 21-24v, luigi (the attribution is not in the hand of the text).

B Bc, F.A.VI 38, ff. 171-174v, anon.

I PAc, CF-111-1, ff. 103v-108, anon.

US CHH, Music Vault M2.1.M1, ff. 53v-56v, anon.

72.   Fanciulla son io ch'amare non sa. Wo. 66, Gh. 93, Re. 33.

F Pn, Rés. Vm7 102, ff. 111-113v, Luigi, text by Domenico Benigni. (The refrain is varied musically with each repetition.)

GB Och, 17, ff. 13v-14, anon. (The refrain, here too, is varied. The key is G major. The first strophe differs melodically and rhythmically in several measures from the other versions, and the second strophe is not set to the same music of the first as it is in all the other sources, but is set to a variation of it. The third and fourth strophes are omitted.)

F Pn, Vm7 10, ff. 16v-17, anon. (The refrain is not varied. Numerous measures differ melodically and rhythmically from the corresponding measures in the other sources.)

I Rc, 2479, ff. 19-24v, anon. (as Rés. Vm7 102).

I Rc, 2505, ff. 57v-61v, anon.

GB Lbm, Harl. 7549, ff. 10-10v, anon. (The refrain is not varied. The key is F major; the note values are doubled. A number of measures also differ melodically and rhythmically from the other sources. The continuo and the second, third, and fourth strophes are missing.)

B Bc, F 664, pp. 55-58; 28072, pp. 55-59 (copies of Rés. Vm7 102).

N, pp. 97-104; Gv, II, 122 ff.

73.   Fanciulle, tenete il guard'a voi. Gh. 94.

F Psg, MS 3372, ff. 47v-48v, Luigi.
I Nc, 33.4.7, ff. 101-106, Luigi Rossi.
I Rvat, Chigi Q IV 8, ff. 88-89, anon.
B Br, *Canzonette amorose* . . . (Rotterdam: Giovanni Van Geertsom, 1656),
Basso continuo part, p. 5, anon.

74.   Fate quel che volete, begl'occhi. Wo. 67, Gh. 96.

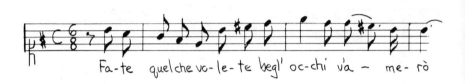

F Pn, Vm7 6, f. 4v, Luigi Rossi.
F Pthibualt, Rec.H.P.4, ff. 48v-49v, anon. (the attribution Luigi Rossi is
a later addition in pencil).
F Pa, M.948, ff. 15-16v, anon. (in d minor and without a second strophe;
in this source the last eighth note of the second measure is raised a
half-step).
I Rc, 2475, ff. 31-33v, anon.
B Bc, 15261, pp. 69-70 (copy of Vm7 6).
Pm, III, 12-14.
Another setting for soprano solo:
I MOe, Mus.E.279, ff. 44v-46v, Cappellini.

75.   Ferma Giove, ferma, non piover piu.

I Rdp, 51, pp. 25-32, Luigi Rossi.

76.　Fillide mia, deh, come tu mi comparti infidi i tuoi conforti.·

I Rc, 2478, ff. 12-16v, Luigi Rossi.
F Psg, MS 3372, ff. 18v-21v, Luigi.

77.　Fingi ch'io t'ho tradito, Filli.

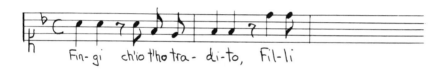

I Rbn, 71.9.A, ff. 111-118v, Luigi Rossi.
Another setting for soprano solo:
I Rvat, Chigi Q IV 3, ff. 10-15v, anon.
I Nc, 33.3.11, ff. 81-84, anon.
I Bc, Q 46, ff. 5-7, anon.

78.　Gelosia che à poco à poco. Wo. 72, Gh. 101, Re. 81.

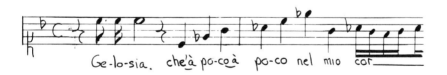

F Pn, Rés, Vm7 59, ff. 103-108v, Luigi Rossi, text by Domenico Benigni.
GB Lbm, Harl. 1265, ff. 79-86v, Luige Rossi.
B Bc, F.A.VI 38, ff. 57-64v, anon.
I Rvat, Barb. lat. 4175, ff. 49v-59, anon.
US SFdeBellis, MS Misc. V.LXIX, ff. 60v-67, anon.

B Bc, F 664, pp. 1-8; XY 8286, pp. 73-75 (copies of Rés. Vm7 59).
US Wc, *Ariette di Musica* . . . (Bracciano, 1646), pp. 31-36, Luigi Rossi,
   Musico dell'Eminentiss. Card. Ant. Barberino.
Gv, I, 39 ff.

The text is published in G. A. Cesareo, *Poesie e lettere edite ed inedite
di Salvator Rosa* (Naples, 1892), I, 136, with the text of *Questo picciol rio*
(below, no. 159). Cesareo's source for the attribution is Burney; *A General History* (Dover edition, 1957), II, 618-622, who, however, says nothing
about the text of either of these pieces. Limentani, op. cit., p. 14, and
Frank Walker, "Salvator Rosa and Music," *Monthly Musical Record*,
LXXIX (1949), p. 201, explain that Cesareo misread Burney's descriptions of the pieces in Salvator Rosa's book as descriptions of the pieces
by Luigi in Harl. 1265. Several short musical examples from the latter are
given by Burney without mention of their source. It is probable that this
omission confused Cesareo.

79.   Già finita è per me d'amor ogni fortuna. Wo. 73, Gh. 104.

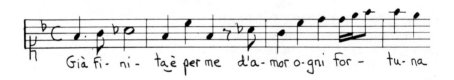

F Pn, Vm7 6, f. 3, Luigi Rossi.
I Rvat, Barb. lat. 4175, ff. 77v-79, anon.
B Bc, 15261, pp. 51-52 (copy of Vm7 6).

80.   Già nell'oblio profondo il dì sepolto giace. Wo. 74, Gh. 106, Re. 82.

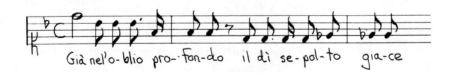

GB Lbm, Harl. 1265, ff. 108-113, Luige.
B Bc, 17193, pp. 147-151 (copy of Harl. 1265).

81.   Giusto così va detto. Adesso siete il cauto. Wo. 76, Gh. 109.

GB Lbm, Harl. 1265, ff. 95-104, luige.
B Bc, F.A., VI 38, ff. 93-104v, anon.

82.   Guardatevi, olà! nemica io sono. Wo. 77, Gh. 110, Re. 34.

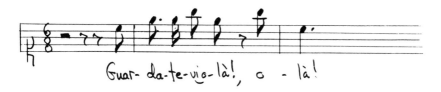

B Br, II 3947, ff. 95-98v, Luigi Rossi.
I Rsc, G 885, ff. 49-52, del d° (Luigi Rossi).
B Bc, F 664, pp. 9-11; XY 8286, p. 76; 28072, pp. 11-13 (copies of II 3947).
Eins 87 20-21 (copy of II 3947).
F Pn, Vm7 6 is listed as a source in Wotquenne's catalogue and in Ghislanzoni's. I have examined the MS but did not find *Guardatevi, olà!* there, nor does Ecorcheville, op. cit, VII, 180-189, list it among the pieces in Vm7 6.

83.   Ho perduto la fortuna che fuggendo ogn'hor mi va. Wo. 117, Gh. 111.

F Pn, Vm7 6, f. 1, Luigi Rossi.
I Rvat, Barb. lat. 4208, ff. 19-20v, anon.
F Pa, M. 948, ff. 51-53, anon.
B Bc, 15261, p. 27 and pp. 3-4 (copy of Vm7 6). The second part, "Pensieri dolenti" is copied separately. Wotquenne, having mistaken it for an independent piece, remarks that though anonymous it is without doubt by Luigi Rossi.

"Pensieri dolenti" is also listed as an independent piece by Ecorcheville, op. cit., VII, 182. The attribution Luigi Rossi here is an error. In the MS no attribution is placed above "Pensieri dolenti."

84.   Hora ch'ad ecclissar la luna audace dell'Ottomano infido. Gh. 178.

I Rdp, 51, ff. 1-7, Luigi Rossi.
I Rvat, Barb. lat. 4208, ff. 92-95v, anon.

85.   Horch'avvolte in fosco velo stan le cure.

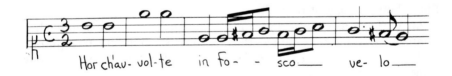

I Rsc, G 885, ff. 41-44, del d° (Luigi Rossi).

86.   Horche di marte il grido con bellicosi carmi.

I Rc, 2479, ff. 119-120v, L.R.

87.   Horche la notte del silentio amica. Wo. 119, Gh. 179.

Pietro Della Valle in his letter "Della musica dell'eta nostra"[4] mentions as an example of the serious kind of new music sung at the time (1640)[5] the "canzonetta" by Luigi which begins with the words quoted above. Scholars[6] cite this reference by Della Valle, but say the music is lost.[7] The writer, however, found an anonymous setting in I Rbn, 56, ff. 19v-20v and again ff. 59v-63v where it is more complete.[8] It is highly probable that the music is Luigi's. The author of the text is not known.[9]

88.   Horche l'oscuro manto della notte ricopre il ciel. Wo. 118, Gh. 180.

GB Och, 946, ff. 47-52v, Luigi.
I SPc, MS 13906 (MS 1), ff. 38-45v
   (half of f. 44 is torn away), anon.

Recorded in "Chamber Music for Soprano and Continuo," Pleiades Records, P 103.

89.   Horch'io vivo lontano dal mio ben, dal mio cor. Wo. 120, Gh. 181, Re. 90.

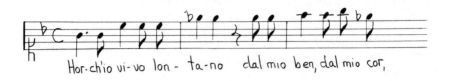

Hor-ch'io vi-vo lon - ta-no   dal mio ben, dal mio cor,

F Pn, Rés. Vm7 102, ff. 95-100v, Luigi Rossi.
B Bc, 17192, pp. 104-115 (copy of Rés. Vm7 102).

90.   Hor guardate come và la fortuna.

Hor guar-da-te co-me   và, co-me và la For - tu - na

F Pthibault, G.T.3, ff. 83-88v, Luigi Rossi.
I Nc, 33.4.17, II, 9-14v, anon.

91.   Hor si, versate, o lumi, d'aspre lagrime.

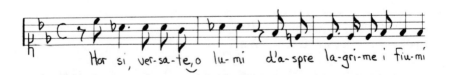

Hor si, ver-sa-te,o lu-mi   d'a-spre la-gri-me i fiu-mi

F Pthibault, Libro di Salvator Rosa, no. 6, Luigi.
I Rc, 2480, ff. 171-182v, Luigi Rossi.

92. Ho vinto, gridava amore. La mia possanza. Wo. 122, Gh. 122, Re. 55.

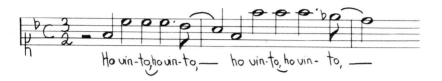

I Rvat and Rsc, *Raccolta d'arie spirituali* . . . (Roma: Vincenzo Bianchi, 1640), p. 17, Luigi de Rossi.
B Bc, 17193, pp. 97-98 (copy of the print).

93. Ho voto di non amare; da lacci il core disciolto. Wo. 123, Gh. 186.

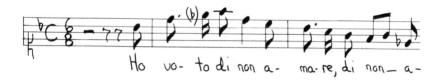

GB Ckc, MS 22, ff. 180v-181v, Luigi Rossi.
F Pc, M. 99, anon.
F Pa, M.948, ff. 3-7v, anon.
GB Och, 947, ff. 45-50, luigi (the attribution is not in the hand of the text).
F Pthibault, Rec. H.P. 4, ff. 53v-55v, anon. (the attribution Luigi Rossi is a recent addition).
I PAc, CF-111-1, ff. 164-171, anon.

94. Il cor mi dice che vicino a morte. Wo. 78, Gh. 113, Re. 56.

I Rvat and Rsc, *Raccolta d'arie spirituali* . . . (Roma: Vincenzo Bianchi, 1640), pp. 18-19, Luigi de Rossi.
B Bc, 17193, pp. 99-100 (copy of the print).

(The second strophe, "Mentre ch'io stringo" is listed by Riemann, no. 67, as a separate piece.)

95.   Ingordo human desio, che con avide brame. Wo. 82, Gh. 118.

GB Och, 998, ff. 205-216v, Luigi Rossi.

96.   In solitario speco, ove l'ipocrisia. Wo. 83, Gh. 121, Re. 19.

F Pn, Rés. Vm7 59, ff. 77-80v, Luigi Rossi, text by Antonio Abbati.
GB Och, 998, ff. 167-174v, Luigi Rossi.
B Bc, 17192, pp. 184-193 (copy of Rés. Vm7 59).

97.   Io che sin hor le piante dell'inospite selve.

F Pthibault, Rec. H.P. 1, ff. 1-6, Luigi Rossi.
I Rvat, Barb. lat. 4146, ff. 6v-8v continues ff. 59v-60, anon. (incomplete).
I Rc, 2505, ff. 51v-54v, anon.
Pm, V, 5-11.

98.   Io ero pargoletta quand'altri mi narrò. Wo. 84, Gh. 123, Re. 66.

I Bc, Q 49, f. 33, Luigi de Rossi di Borghese.
B Bc, 17197, pp. 99-100 (copy of Q 49).
P, pp. 10-11; Su, no. 54.

The text is the first strophe from an aria in the opera *La Flora* by Marco da Gagliano, libretto by Andrea Salvadori, performed in Florence in 1628. (A score is in I Bc). The aria was discussed and printed by Luigi Torchi, "Canzoni ed Arie italiane ad una voce nel secolo XVII," *RMI*, I (1894), pp. 639-641. Torchi speaks of Luigi's setting (pp. 641-642) and quotes part of it. His opinion is that no one would prefer Luigi's music. The fact is that each of the settings has its merits. The version by Marco da Gagliano is also published in Torchi, *Eleganti canzoni ed arie italiane del secolo XVII* (Milano, 1893), pp. 37-38.

The attribution Luigi de Rossi di Borghese indicates that at the time MS Q 49 was compiled Luigi was employed by the Borghese family in Rome. The date of his departure from Naples to reside in Rome is presumed to be about 1620. (Ghislanzoni, op. cit., p. 24.) It is probable that he was associated with the Borghese until 1640. (Ibid., p. 39.) Since Luigi's setting of *Io ero pargoletta* must date after the performance of the opera (Oct. 14, 1628), and since the contents, mostly short strophic pieces, are stylistically of the first third of the century, the MS most certainly was compiled sometime in the third decade.

99.   Io lo vedo, o luci belle. Wo. 85, Gh. 124, Re. 35.

B Br, II, 3947, ff. 121-124v, Luigi Rossi (lacks text of 1st strophe).
I Rvat, Barb. lat. 4150, ff. 91-92v, anon.
B Bc, 17193, pp. 40-43 (copy of II 3947).
Eins, 87, 26 (copy of II 3947).
HAM, II, 40 (poorly edited).

100.   Io non amo, sì, ma cerco nel core l'imago. Wo. 86, Gh. 125.

I Rc, 2468, ff. 193-196v, Luigi Rossi.
I Rc, 2475, ff. 87-90v, anon.
B Bc, 11008, pp. 18-22 (copy of 2468).

101.   Io piangea presso d'un rio e pietoso al mio tormento. Gh. 122.

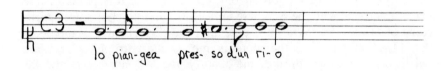

GB Och, 948, ff. 30-40, Luiggi Rossi.
I Nc, 33.4.12, ff. 1-10v, Luigi Rossi.

102. La bella che mi contenta ha volto che spira amore.

La bel-la che mi con-ten-ta

I Rsc, G 885, ff. 45-48v, del d° (Luigi Rossi).

103. La bella per cui son cieco languisce per me. Gh. 126, Re. 57.

La bel-la per cui son cie-co lan-gui-sce per me

I Rvat, Barb. lat. 4163, ff. 7v-10, Luigi.
F Pthibault, Rec. H.P.4, ff. 59v-61, anon. (the attribution Luigi Rossi is
   a later addition).
I MOe, Mus. F 1382, ff. 55-56, anon.
B Bc, 17197, pp. 154-156 (copy of 4163).

104. La bella più bella che il cor mi ferí. Wo. 87, Gh. 127, Re. 72.

La bel-la più bel-la chil cor mi fe-rì.

F Pn, Rés. Vm7 102, ff. 114-116v, Luigi Rossi, text by the Principe di
   Cola d'Anchise.
I Rvat, Chigi Q IV 3, ff. 16-20v, anon.
B Bc, F 664, pp. 63-66; 28072, pp. 63-67 (copies of Rés. Vm7 102).

105.   Lascia, speranza, ohimè, ch'io mi lamenti. Wo. 90, Gh. 130, Re. 84.

B Br, II 3947, ff. 31-38v, Luigi Rossi.
F Pn, Rés, Vm7 102, ff. 147-150v, Luigi Rossi, text by Domenico Benigni.
I Rvat, Chigi Q IV 5, ff. 80-83, anon.
I Rc, 2505, ff. 79-82v, anon.
US CA, MS Mus 108, no. 8, ff. (31-34v), anon.
B Bc, 17193, pp. 19-26 (copy of II 3947).
Eins., 87, 7-8 (copy of II 3947).

106.   Lasciate ch'io ritorni a miei lamenti. Wo. 91, Gh. 131, Re. 85.

GB Lbm, Harl. 1265, ff. 114-124, Luigi Rossi.
B Bc, 17193, pp. 139-144 (copy of Harl. 1265).

107.   Lasciatemi qui solo, speranze venturate. Wo. 92, Gh. 132, Re. 86.

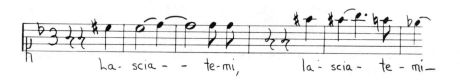

F Pn, Rés, Vm7 102, ff. 143-146v, Luigi Rossi, text by Domenico Benigni.
I Rc, 2480, ff. 193-198v, Del d° (Luigi Rossi).
US CA, MS Mus 106, no. 14, ff. (53-56v), anon.

US SFdeBellis, MS Misc. V.LXIX, ff. 48v-52, anon.
B Bc, F 664, pp. 21-27; 28072, pp. 20-27 (copies of Rés. Vm7 102).

108.   Luci belle, dite, ohime, che siete. Wo. 93, Gh. 134, Re. 67.

GB Lbm, Harl. 1501, ff. 31-31v, Luiggi Rossi (lacks 2d and 3d strophes).
I Rc, 2482, ff. 24-24v, skip to 26-30v, anon. (mistakenly listed as a con-
cordance with attribution in Ghislanzoni's catalogue).
US CA, MS Mus 106, no. 13, ff. (49-52v), anon.
B Bc, 17197, pp. 117-118 (copy of Harl. 1501).

109.   Luci mie, da me sparite, s'il pregarvi non è ardire. Wo. 94, Gh. 135,
Re. 87.

I MOe, Mus. G. 172, Luiggi Rossi.
I Nc, 33.4.19, ff. 75-80v, anon.
B Bc, 17193, pp. 57-61 (copy of G 172).

Ghislanzoni lists I Bc, MS 950 as a source with attribution. There is no
MS 950 at the Conservatory library in Bologna, nor is there a copy of
Luci mie in any of the MSS there.

110.   Lungi da me, mio bene, idolo di quest'alma. Wo. 95, Gh. 136.

B Br, II 3947, ff. 67-70v, Luigi Rossi.
B Bc, 17193, pp. 30-33 (copy of II 3947).
Eins, 87, 14-15 (copy of II 3947).

111.   Mai finirò d'amare bench'io soffra.

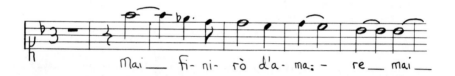

GB Ouf, MS U.210.4, ff. 23-30, Luigi Rossi.
F Pthibault, G.T.3, ff. 1-10v, Luigi Rossi.
F Pn, Vm7 6, ff. 6v-7, anon.
B Bc, 15261, pp. 42-45 (copy of Vm7 6 made by Wotquenne who, not
   knowing of the MS G.T.3, remarks that though anonymous the piece
   is certainly Luigi Rossi's).

112.   Mai no'l dirò chi sia quel core, quel possessore. Wo. 96, Gh. 138.

I Rc, 2468, ff. 109-112v, Luigi Rossi.
GB Och, 949, ff. 45-48v, Luigi.
F Pn, Vm7 17, pp. 90-91, Luigi.

I Rc, 2475, ff. 114-116v, anon.
B Bc, 15261, pp. 63-64 (copy of Vm7 17).

113. Mani altere e divine, amor per farvi belle.

GB Och, 17, ff. 10-11, Luigi (in C major; lacks 2d strophe).
I Rvat, Barb. lat. 4200, ff. 33v-35, anon.

—Mentre ch'io stringo il nodo. Re. 67.

See Il cor mi dice che vicino a morte, no. 94 above.

114. Mentre sorge dal mare la bella aurora. Gh. 141.

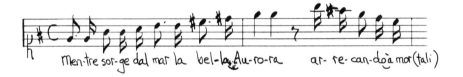

I RC, 2466, ff. 37-46v, Luigi Rossi.
I Rc, 2475, ff. 129-138v, anon.
I Rvat, Barb. lat. 4208, ff. 46v-50, anon.

115. Mi contento così, se sciolse i lumi al pianto.

I Rdp, 51, pp. 33-36, Luigi Rossi.
F Pn, Vm7 1, ff. 75-81, anon.

116.   Mi danno la morte due luci severe. Gh. 143.

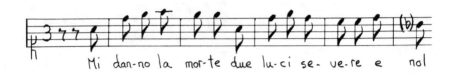

I Nc, 33.4.15, I, 117-128v, Luigi Rossi.

117.   Mio core languisce e mai non si more. Wo. 97, Gh. 145, Re. 36.

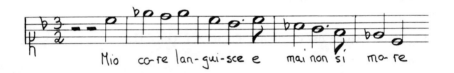

F Pn, Rés. Vm7 102, ff. 61-63v, Luigi Rossi, text by Domenico Benigni.
I Rc, 2479, ff. 81-96, anon.
I Rc, 2505, ff. 55-57v, anon.
F Pc, Rés. 2096, pp. 126-127, anon. (lacks continuo; the meter is ¾.
B Bc, F 664, pp. 35-38; 28072, pp. 32-36 (copies of Vm7 102).

118.   Misero cor, perche pensando vai. Gh. 146, Re. 59.

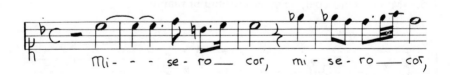

I Nc, 33.4.12, ff. 121-126, Luigi Rossi.
B Bc, 17197, pp. 160-162 (copy of 33.4.12).

119.   Mostro con l'ali nere, col crin di serpi. Wo. 98, Gh. 148, Re. 88.

F Pn, Rés, Vm7 102, ff. 55-60v, Luigi Rossi, text by Fabio della Cornia.
I Rc, 2483, ff. 31-46v, Luigi Rossi.
B Bc, 17192, pp. 116-131 (copy of Rés. Vm7 102).

120.   M'uccidete, begl'occhi, e pur v'adoro. Wo. 99, Gh. 149.

I Rc, 2477, ff. 175-180v, Luigi Rossi.
F Pn, Vm7 17, pp. 79-85, Luigi.
F Pa, M.948, ff. 19-21v, anon. (lacks text of second strophe).
F Pn, Vm7 6, ff. 6-6v, anon.
B Bc, 15261, pp. 46-47 (copy of Vm7 6).

121.   Nel dì che al Padre eterno se stesso il Figlio. Wo. 100, Gh. 150.

GB Och, 998, ff. 113-136v, Luigi Rossi.
A Wn, 18610, ff. 1-9v, anon. (has the title "Peccatore pentito").
B Bc, 12900, pp. 1-12 (copy of 18610).

Ghislanzoni believes *Nel di che al Padre eterno* is part of the cantata-oratorio *Il Peccatore Pentito*, though it is not in any of the MSS containing the various pieces that form *Il Peccatore Pentito*.[10] Nowhere is there an indication that Giovanni Lotti, author of the cantata-oratorio, is author of *Nel di che al Padre eterno*. Ghislanzoni was probably misled by the title "Peccatore pentito." Many texts of the seventeenth century deal with the penitent sinner; there are several independent compositions like *Nel di* that are concerned with the subject, e.g., *Reo d'impuniti eccessi* (I Rvat, 4203, ff. 87-92v) has the title "Un peccatore a Piedi un Crocifisso." "Un peccator pentito" is the subject of *Bellezza nel mio cor* (I Rvat, 4200, ff. 13-17v). *Voi per ultima aita* (I Rvat Barb. lat. 4219, ff. 16-24) is also about "Un peccator pentito." In Lotti's *Poesie*, op. cit., pp. 142-146, the title "Peccatore a Piedi del Crocefisso" precedes the poem *Prestatemi l'ardore*. (The rubric "Aria a 2" indicates the poem may have been set to music.)

122.   Ne notte ne dì riposa quest'alma. Wo. 101, Gh. 151, Re. 37.

D. SW, 4718a, pp. 77-79, Luigi (lacks text of 2d strophe).
GB Lbm, Harl. 1273, f. 76v, Luigi Rossi (lacks text of 2d strophe).
I Rvat, Barb. lat. 4163, ff. 13-15v, anon.
D Mbs, 1524, ff. 16-19, anon.
F Pc, Rés. 2096, pp. 136-137, anon. (lacks continuo).
B Bc, 17193, pp. 191-192 (copy of Harl. 1273).

Following *Ne notte ne dì* on p. 79 of the MS 4718a, but separated from it by two empty staves, is the beginning of the soprano aria, *No, no, no, no, fuggir non vo*. It is anonymous. Following *Ne notte ne dì* in Harl. 1273 is the same aria, but here the rubric "segue" is placed between the end of *Ne notte* and the beginning of the aria, as if the aria were a continuation of *Ne notte*. The copyist, copying from 4718a or from a source identical with it,[11] was misled by the absence of any "Fine" sign (either the word or a series of vertical lines, or a bold swirling line), by the absence of an attribution before *No, no*, and by its presence on the same page with *Ne notte*. He may also have been misled by the fact that both pieces have the tonic G, but the first is in the minor mode; the second in the major. The two pieces are independent of one another; each is complete in itself. The second is a two-part form. The first has the form A b C A b C A, A being the refrain; b, the strophe; C, a verse repeated as a motto at the end of the second strophe. The second strophe (omitted in 4718a and in Harl. 1273) is sung to the same music as the first. The metrical form of the text of *No, no* is completely different from that of *Ne notte*. The complaint of an unhappy lover is the subject of both texts, but the second is not a continuation of the first. The fact that the text of *No, no, no, no, fuggir non vo* is inserted in an opera libretto completely independent of *Ne notte ne di* further proves that the two are separate and distinct pieces. See also below, no. 358.

(The second strophe "Quando niega la luce" which Wotquenne and Ghislanzoni say is an additional strophe in the MS 1524 is also in MSS Barb. lat. 4163 and Rés. 2096.)

123.　Nessun sene vanti di viver disciolto.

I Rc, 2468, ff. 197-200v, Luigi Rossi.

124.　Nò, mio bene, non lo dite ch'altre fiamme. Wo. 102, Gh. 153, Re. 59a.

F Pn, Rés. Vm7 102, ff. 155bis-156bisv, Luigi Rossi, text by Domenico Benigni.
I Rvat, Barb. lat. 4175, ff. 73v-77, anon.

B Bc, F664, pp. 43-46; 28072, pp. 43-46 (copies of Rés. Vm7 102).
US CA, MS Mus 106, no. 34, ff. (111-112v), anon. (lacks text of 3d strophe).
Another setting, for 2 sopranos and continuo:
I Rc, 2464, ff. 106-109, anon.
I Bc, Q 48, ff. 163-165, anon.

125.   Non c'è che dire, ho da penare. Wo. 103, Gh. 154.

GB Och, 949, ff. 73-76v, Luigi.

—Non ha core, no. Gh. 156.

See Sopra conca d'argento, no. 177, below.

126.   Non la volete intendere, ostinati pensieri.

I Rc, 2466, ff. 185-188v, Luigi.
   The attribution is not in the hand of the text, but in the hand that appears earlier in the MS on ff. 109-112 (*Con amor si pugna*, no. 48), and later, on ff. 209-216 (*Se non corre una speranza*, no. 170). In the same hand is the attribution Luigi on f. 59 at the beginning of *Ve, ve che miro*, though the text is in yet another hand. Since the attributions are in the hand of one of the copyists of the MS, and since one of the attributions is verified by a concordance, they seem reliable.
I Nc, 33.5.18, ff. 76-78v, anon. (the attribution Bassi is a later addition).

La, pp. 28-32 (the source is MS 2466).

127.   Non m'affligete più, vani pensieri. Wo. 105, Gh. 157.

I Rvat, US NYp, GB Lbm, *Scelta di Canzonette . . .* (London: A. Godbid,
& J. Playford, 1679) pp. 13-19, Luigi Rossi.
B Bc, 17196, pp. 6-8 (copy of the print).
Another setting for soprano solo:
I MOe, Camp. App. 1998, anon.

128.   Non mi fate mentire. Ho già detto a ciascun. Wo. 107, Gh. 159,
Re. 7.

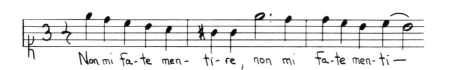

D SW, 4718a, pp. 95-97, Luigi (lacks text of 2d strophe).
B Bc, 17197, pp. 22-23 (copy of 4718a).

Wotquenne lists I Rvat, Barb. lat. 4200, ff. 176-181, as an anonymous
concordance, but, as Ghislanzoni indicates, this is another setting of the
text. It is a duet for two sopranos related musically to Luigi's solo piece.
See below, no. 420.
A third setting, for soprano:
F Pc, Res. 2096, pp. 116-117, anon. (lacks continuo).

129.   Nò, nò, non ci pensa, nò; lusingar, core, ti vuoi.

I Rc, 2467, ff. 32v-38, Luigi, text by Principe del Colle d'Anchise.

130.   Non più viltà, non più timore, ardisci, mio core. Wo. 108, Gh. 163, Re. 89.

GB Lbm, Harl. 1501, ff. 69v-71v, Luiggi Rossi.
I Bc, Q 47, ff. 99-103, anon.
F Pn, Vm7 1, ff. 1-16v, anon.

131.   Non sarà, non fù, non è un'amante più costante. Wo. 109, Gh. 164.

F Pn, Vm7 17, pp. 109-118, Luigi Rossi.
B Bc, 15261, pp. 65-68 (copy of Vm7 17).

132.   Non ti doler, mio core, se la beltà.

I MAC, MS Mus. 78, ff. 166-175v, S. Luige.

133.   Occhi ardenti, pupille belle ch'ardete divisi in due poli. Wo. 111,

GB Och, 949, ff. 69-72v, Luigi.
Another setting for soprano solo:
I Nc, 33.4.18, ff. 127-130, Savioni.
I Nc, 33.4.4, no. 53, anon.
F Pn, Vm7 1, ff. 114-117v, anon.

134.   Occhi belli, occhi vezzosi, dove Amor pose l'impero. Wo. 112,
Gh. 170.

GB Och, 949, ff. 77-79, Luigi.
I Rc, 2468, ff. 113-116v, Luigi Rossi.
I Rc, 2475, ff. 47-49v, anon.

135.   O dura più d'un sasso, ò più fredda del gielo. Wo. 113, Gh. 172.

GB Och, 950, ff. 21-30v, Luigi.
Another version for soprano solo:
I Nc, 33.5.16, ff. 126-136, Carissimi.
D K1, 2° Mus. 34, ff. 2-3v, anon. (the first folio is missing). Wotquenne
    and Ghislanzoni erroneously give 2° Mus. 34 as a concordance of Luigi's
    setting.
I Vqs, Cl. VIII, cod. 15, ff. 52v-55v, anon.

136.   O grotta, o speco, o sasso, caro porto giocondo. Gh. 173.

I Rvat, Chigi Q IV 18, ff. 69-80v, Luigi Rossi.

137.   Ohimè, Madre, aita, aita! Già nel cor mi sento un foco. Wo. 115,
    Gh. 175, Re. 38.

F Psg, MS 3372, ff. 23-24v, Luigi Rossi.
GB Lbm, Harl. 1501, ff. 15v-16v, Luiggi Rossi.
I Rvat, Barb. lat. 4200, ff. 65v-67, anon.

I Nc, 33.4.19, ff. 39-41v, anon.
B Bc, 17197, pp. 114-116 (copy of Harl. 1501).
Another setting for soprano solo (has text for a 2d strophe omitted in
  Luigi's version):
GB Och, 998, ff. 201-203v, Mario Savioni.

138.   Olà, pensieri, olà! Il varco del mio core. Gh. 176.

I Nc, 33.4.12, ff. 155-160v, Luigi Rossi.
F Pthibault, Rec.H.P.6, pp. 6-11, anon.

Ghislanzoni gives I Rvat, Barb. lat. 4136 as a source with an anonymous
concordance, but only the first words, "Olà, pensieri," are the same.
The music is entirely different.

139.   Ombre, fuggite, e voi, notturni orrori. Wo. 116, Gh. 177.

GB Och, 950, ff. 31-42v, Luigi.

140.   Orrida e solitaria era una selva. Wo. 121, Gh. 182, Re. 8.

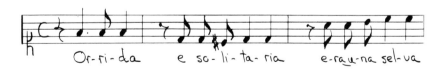

D SW, 4718a, pp. 49-59, Luigi.
B Bc, 17197, pp. 14-20 (copy of 4718a).
Another setting, for tenor solo:
A Wn, 17763, ff. 184-191v, anon.

141.   Partii dal gioire già venni alle pene. Wo. 124, Gh. 187.

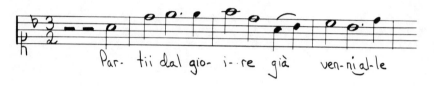

F Pn, Vm7 17, pp. 94-95, Luigi.
B Bc, 15261, p. 61 (copy of Vm7 17).

142.   Patienza, tocca a me di languir sempre così. Gh. 189.

I Rc, 2466, ff. 117-124v, Luigi.
I Rvat, Barb. lat. 4208, ff. 50v-54, anon.
GB Och, 959, ff. 21-27v, anon.

143.   Pender non prima vide sopra vil tronco. Wo. 126, Gh. 190.

GB Och, 998, ff. 79-92v, del dº (Luigi Rossi).

A Wn, 18610, ff. 29-34, anon. (has the title "Pianto della Madalena").
B Bc, 12900, pp. 38-45 (copy of 18610).

—Pensieri dolenti
See Ho perduta la fortuna, no. 83 above.

144.   Pensoso, afflitto, irresoluto e solo. Wo. 127, Gh. 191, Re. 17.

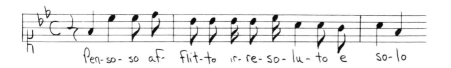

GB Cfm, 24.F.4, ff. 97-98v, Luigi Rossi.
GB Lbm, Harl. 1264, ff. 1-6v, anon. (Ghislanzoni, by error, lists this as
   a source with attribution.)
I Busseto, Villa Verdi, an unclassified MS dated 1689 whose folios are not
   numbered; the anonymous version of the cantata given here is considerably longer than that in the other MSS sources.
B Bc, 17193, pp. 183-187 (copy of 24.F.4).

Wotquenne and Ghislanzoni list A Wn, 18610 as a source with an anonymous concordance, but *Pensoso, afflitto* is not in this MS.

145.   Perchè chieder com'io stò mentr'il puoi saper. Wo. 128, Gh. 192,
       Re. 39.

B Br, II 3947, ff. 41-44, Luigi Rossi.
F Pc, Rés. 2096, pp. 66-67, Luigi (lacks text of 3d strophe and lacks
   continuo part).
B Bc, 17193, pp. 26-29 (copy of II 3947).

Eins, 87, 9 (copy of II 3947).

146.   Perchè ratto così il lampo del sole.

I Rc, 2467, ff. 94v-102v, Luigi.
I Rvat, Barb. lat. 4175, ff. 120-126v, anon.

147.   Perchè speranze, ohimè! perchè tornate. Wo. 129, Gh. 193, Re. 91.

F Pn, Rés. Vm7 59, ff. 85-90v, Luigi Rossi, text by Domenico Benigni.
I Rc, 2505, ff. 32v-40, anon.
B Bc, 17192, pp. 68-83 (copy of Rés, Vm7 59).

148.   Precorrea del sol l'uscita la bell'alba in Oriente. Wo. 132, Gh. 197,
        Re. 92.

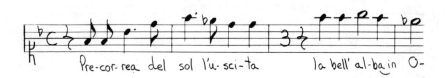

I Rvat, Chigi Q VII 99, ff. 64v-67v, Luige Rossi.
F Pn, Rés. Vm7 59, ff. 81-84v, Luigi Rossi, text by Domenico Benigni.

B Bc, 17192 pp. 84-93 (copy of Rés. Vm7 59).

Ghislanzoni gives I Rvat, Chigi Q IV 18 as a source with a concordance attributed to Rossi, but *Precorrea del sol* is not there.

149.   Presso un ruscel sedea un huom di crin canuto. Gh. 198.

I Rvat, Chigi Q IV 11, ff. 153-162v, Luigi Rossi.
GB Och, 949, ff. 61-68v, Luigi.
GB Lbm, R.M. 24 i 11, no. 22, luigi (the attribution is not in the hand of
   the text).
I Rc, 2466, ff. 175-182v, anon.
I Rvat, Barb. lat. 4208, ff. 29-33v, anon.
I MOe, Mus. G 41, Carissimi, text by Benigni.

Wotquenne lists *Presso un ruscel* under "Oeuvres douteuses ou apocryphes."

150.   Pria ch'al sdegno tu mi desti, figlio vano. Gh. 199.

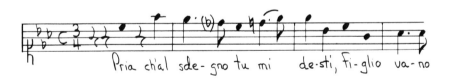

I Rdp, 51, pp. 141-145, Luigi Rossi.
I Rvat, Chigi Q IV 13, ff. 17-24v, Luigi Rossi.
I Nc, 33.5.18, ff. 71-75v, anon. (the attribution Abt. Bassi is a later
   addition).

151.   Quando Florinda bella s'avvide che partito. Gh. 201.

I Nc, 33.5.33, ff. 81v-85v, Luiggi Rossi.

152.   Quando meco tornerai, libertà da me sparita.

I Rbn, 71.9.A.33, ff. 231v-234v, Luigi.
Another setting for soprano solo (lacks text for 2d strophe).
I Rvat, Barb. lat. 4201, ff. 37v-39, anon.
I Rvat, Barb. lat. 4221, ff. 105-107, anon.

153.   Quando mi chiede amore s'io sarò sempre amante.

F Pthibault, Libro di Salvator Rosa, no. 7 (ff. 19-22), Luigi (for soprano
   and continuo).
I Rvat, Barb. lat. 4374, ff. 1-10, anon. (for tenor and continuo).
Another version for solo voice:
I Rvat, Chigi Q VIII 177, ff. 77v-80, anon. (Marco Marazzoli).

A part of the text, beginning with the verse "E se natura avara," is
published by Lady Sidney Morgan, op. cit., I, 305, with the comment

that the poem is a proof of Rosa's truth, devotion, and sincerity in love. G. A. Cesareo, op. cit., I, 137, publishes the text, expressing doubt that Salvator Rosa is its author. Limentani's opinion, op. cit, pp. 15-16, also is that there is no reason to believe that the text is Rosa's. Although the pieces occurs in Rosa's "Libro di Musica," there is, in fact, no evidence that the text is his.

154.　Quando più mia libertà si vantava esser sicura.

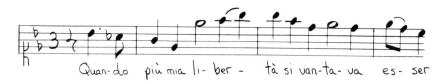

I G1, A-5 Cass., ff. 149-152, Luigi.

155.　Quando spiega la notte humida l'ali. Wo. 133, Gh. 202, Re. 93.

F Pn, Rés. Vm7 102, ff. 117-120v, Luigi Rossi.
GB Lbm, Harl. 1265, ff. 74-78v, Luige.
B Bc, 17192, pp. 94-103 (copy of Rés. Vm7 102).

156.　Quante volte l'ho detto, cor mio, non amar tanto. Wo. 134, Gh. 203, Re. 70.

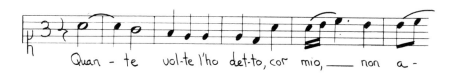

GB Lbm, Harl. 1265, ff. 105-106v, Luige.
B Bc, 17193, pp. 135-136 (copy of Harl. 1265).

157.   Quanto è credulo il mio core! Wo. 135, Gh. 204, Re. 94.

F Pn, Vm7 17, pp. 101-108, Luigi.
B Bc, F 664 (not 17192 as Riemann and Ghislanzoni indicate), pp. 39-42;
    28072, pp. 37-42 (copies of Vm7 17).

158.   Querelatevi di me se vi miro mai più. Wo. 136, Gh. 205.

I Gl, A-5-Cass., ff. 60-65, Luigi.
GB Och, 949, ff. 41-44, Luigi.

159.   Questo picciolo rio che con lingua d'argento. Wo. 137, Gh. 206.

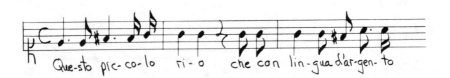

F Pn, Rés. Vm7 102, ff. 73-78v, Luigi Rossi, text by Abbate Bentivoglio
    (the attribution of the text seems to be a later addition).

GB Lbm, Harl. 1265, ff. 63-73, Luige.

On folio 71, at the beginning of the fourth strophe "Stelle che rimiraste," the attribution Luigi Rossi occurs as it would at the beginning of a new piece. Gevaert, misled by this attribution, lists "Stelle che rimiraste" as a separate piece in his notebook (B Bc, XY 8286, p. 70 and p. 134).

I MOe, Mus. G 302, ff. 1-8, anon.

B Bc, F. A. VI 38, ff. 37-44v, anon.

The text is published in G. A. Cesareo, *Poesie e lettere* . . ., I, 136. (See above, no. 78).

160.   Ragion mi dice: lascia d'amare, sarai felice. Wo. 138, Gh. 207, Re. 60.

F Pn, Rés. Vm7 59, ff. 117-118v, Luigi Rossi.

I Rvat, Barb. lat. 4175, ff. 24v-27, anon.

B Bc, F 664, pp. 17-19; 28072, pp. 17-19 (copies of Rés. Vm7 59).

161.   Ravvolse il volo e si librò su l'ali. Wo. 139, Gh. 208, Re. 95.

F Pn, Rés. Vm7 102, ff. 19-26v, Luigi Rossi, text by Fabio della Cornia.

B Bc, 17192, pp. 50-67 (copy of Rés. Vm7 102).

Gevaert (B Bc, XY 8286, p. 67), Wotquenne and Ghislanzoni infer that the cantata was composed sometime during the period of the war between France and Piedmont from the line "where with violent assaults the fierce

Prince of Savoy forbids armed Gaul to take lofty Turin" ("ove tra i fieri assalti vieta l'alta Turino al Gallo armato della Savoia il Principe feroce"). The Prince of Savoy referred to is very likely Carlo Emanuel I, who after 1628 led Piedmont in battle against the French.[12] He died on July 26, 1630, revered and known for his pride and independence.[13] The title "fierce Prince" would not be as appropriate to his successor, Vittorio Amedeo, who concluded the peace treaty of Rivoli with the French in 1635. Thus the text was probably written after 1628 and sometime before July, 1630, for the text refers to the Prince in the present tense.

162.   Rendetevi, pensieri, non contrastate più. Wo. 140, Gh. 209, Re. 40.

F Pn, Rés. Vm7 59, ff. 133-134v, Luigi Rossi, text by Domenico Benigni.
US CA, MS Mus 106, no. 39, ff. (121-122v), anon.
B Bc, 17192, pp. 34-39 (copy of Rés. Vm7 59).

163.   Respira core, forze raduna contra fortuna. Wo. 141, Gh. 210, Re. 41.

I Bc, V/289, ff. 203-204v, Luigi Rossi, text by Domenico Begnigni.
F Pn, Rés. Vm7 59, ff. 137-137v, Luigi Rossi, text Del d° (the attribution Principe Colle d'Anchise is added in pencil, but del d° refers to the name immediately preceding: Domenico Benigni).
F Pthibault, Rec.H.P.31, pp. 201-202 (pp. 181-182 misnumbered), anon. (the attribution Luigi Rossi is added in pencil), lacks text of 2d strophe.
B Bc, F 664, pp. 59-61; 28072, pp. 60-62 (copies of Rés. Vm7 59).

164.   Satiatevi, o cieli, e con man di dolore.

I Bc, V/289, ff. 143-148v, Luigi Rossi, text by Begnigni.

165.   Se dolente e flebil cetra. Gh. 214, Re. 18.

I Nc, 33.4.15, ff. 1-4, Luiggi Rossi.
B Bc, 17197, pp. 158-160 (copy of 33.4.15).
P, pp. 1-4; Su, no. 51.

166.   Sei pur dolce, o libertà! Nulla intende chi ti vende.

F Pthibault, G. T. 3, ff. 79-82v, Luigi Rossi.

167.   Se mai ti punge il seno di duo begl'occhi.

I Rc, 2479, ff. 149-152v, Luigi Rossi. (The attribution is in the hand of the attribution Luigi Rossi on f. 5, and the hand of the second text written below the continuo on ff. 5-18v; it is a hand which is certainly contemporary with the manuscript. See below, no. 196, *Un ferito cavaliero*.)

168.   Se mi volete morto, occhi tiranni. Gh. 216.

Incipit A:

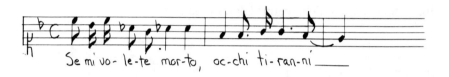

I Nc, 33.4.18, I, 87-100, Luigi Rossi (Incipit A).
GB Och, 953, ff. 1-11, anon. (Incipit A).

Incipit B:

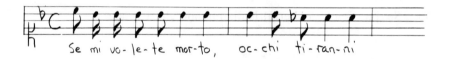

D Lr, K.N.145 Welter S.23, pp. 42-49, anon. (Incipit B).

The first setting of the refrain in the first two sources differs from the second and third settings from its beginning. In Welter S.23 the first setting begins as the second and third settings, but after the tenth bar it continues with the twenty-first to the last measures of the first setting in the other sources.

Wotquenne, knowing only MS 953, lists the piece under "Oeuvres douteuses ou apocryphes."

169.   Se nell'arsura ch'amor ti diede. Wo. 144, Gh. 218.

I Nc, 33.4.7, ff. 107-112, Luigi Rossi.
I Rc, 2466, ff. 65-68v, Luigi Rossi.
B Bc, 11008, pp. 72-75 (copy of 2466).
I Vc, Busta 1-15-N. 11, pp. 21-24, Pasqualini.

170.   Se non corre una speranza à dar vita. Wo. 145, Gh. 219, Re. 9.

I Rc, 2466, ff. 209-216, Luigi Rossi.
I MOe, Mus. G 257, ff. 10-15v, Luigi Rossi.
D Mbs, 1524, ff. 136-144, anon.
B Bc, 17193, pp. 48-53 (copy of Mus. G 257).

Ghislanzoni gives I Bc, Q 50 as a concordance with attribution, but the
cantata is not there. Wotquenne, who knew the MS does not list it as a
concordance.

171.   Sento al cor un non sò che che non fà troppo per me.

I Rsc, G 885, ff. 53-56v, del dº (Luigi Rossi).
GB Och, 951, f. 32v, anon. (text only).

172.   S'era alquanto addormentato per dar tregua. Wo. 147, Gh. 222,
       Re. 10.

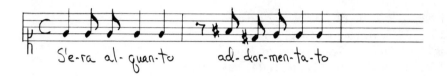

GB Cfm, 24.F.4, ff. 103-105v, Luigi Rossi.
GB Lbm, Harl. 1264, ff. 24-33v, anon.
GB Lbm, Harl. 1863, ff. 115v-121v, anon.
I Rvat, Barb. lat. 4207, ff. 34-40v, anon.
B Bc, 17193, pp. 123-129, Luigi Rossi. (Although Wotquenne omits men-
   tion of his source, a comparison of this copy of his with the four other
   manuscripts reveals that he used MS 24.F.4).
Rk, I, 50-59.
Another setting for soprano solo:
A Wn, 17765, ff. 75-84v, Gioseppe Corsi.
I Nc, 33.4.18, ff. 1-10, Gius(eppe) Corsi.

173.   S'io son vinto, occhi belli, che più da me volete.

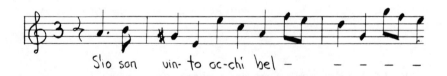

F Psg, MS 3372, ff. 1-2, Luigi Rossi.
US LA, MS fC 697 M4, pp. 22-28, anon. (for soprano and lute).
P, pp. 5-6; Su, no. 52.

174. Sì, v'ingannate, sì. Io senza la mercede. Wo. 148, Gh. 224.

I Nc, 33.4.12, ff. 115-120v, Luigi Rossi.
I Rc, 2477, ff. 29-34v, Luigi.
GB Och, 949, ff. 35-40v, Luigi.
I Gl, A-5-Cass., ff. 7-14, anon.
US CHH, Music Vault M2. 1 M1, ff. 116-119v, anon.

175. Sognai, lasso, sognai che la crudele che tanto amai.

I Rc, 2479, ff. 195-197, Louigi Rossi.

—Sola fra suoi più cari à piè del Figlio afflitto.

I Fbn, Magl. XIX.22, "Cantata del Cav. Marino sopra lo *Stabat Mater*, messa in musica dal medesimo Rossi." The manuscript is lost. See below, no. 384.

176. Son divenuto amante; che pretendete più. Wo. 150, Gh. 227, Re. 71.

I Bc, V/289, ff. 211-212v, del d° (Luigi Rossi), text del d° (Monsignore Vai).
F Pn, Vm7 17, pp. 86-89, Luigi (lacks text of 2d, 3d, and 4th strophes).
I Rvat, Barb. lat. 4175, ff. 91v-94, anon.
B Bc, F 664, pp. 13-15; 28072, pp. 14-16 (copies of Vm7 17).

177.   Sopra conca d'argento la bella Citherea. Gh. 228.

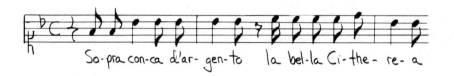

I Bc, V/289, ff. 77-84v, del d° (Luigi Rossi), text del d° (Monsignore Vai).
I Rc, 2480, ff. 183-190, Del d° (Luigi Rossi).
I Rvat, Chigi Q VII 99, ff. 49-53 (=Q VI 87, the MS number given by Cametti and Ghislanzoni).
I Rvat, Barb. lat. 4208, ff. 57v-62, anon.

The second part, "Non ha core, nò," is mistakenly listed as a separate piece by Cametti, "Alcuni documenti . . . ," op. cit., pp. 18-19, and by Ghislanzoni, p. 259, no. 156.

178.   Sospiri miei di foco, ite a quel cor di neve. Wo. 151, Gh. 229, Re. 96.

GB Lbm, Harl. 1265, ff. 167-170, Luigi Rossi ro(mano?).
B Bc, 17193, pp. 131-133 (copy of Harl. 1265).

179. Sospiri, olà, che fate? A che rachiuso in seno. Wo. 152, Gh. 230, Re. 12.

GB Cfm, 24 F 4, ff. 108v-111, Luigi Rossi.
GB Lbm, Harl. 1863, ff. 37-39v, anon.
GB Lbm, Harl. 1264, ff. 58v-64v, anon.
B Bc, 17193 (17192 in Ghislanzoni's catalogue is a misprint), pp. 175-179 (copy of 24 F 4).

180. Sospiri, sù, sù! Giache lo spirto abbandonar mi vuole.

I Rc, 2466, ff. 83-88v, Luigi (the attribution does not seem to be in the hand of the text; it is, however, contemporary with it).

181. Sotto l'ombra d'un pino alto cinque o sei canne. Wo. 153, Gh. 231.

I Bc, V/289, ff. 1-46, Luigi Rossi, text by Monsignore Vai ("Lamento").
GB Och, 998, ff. 1-28v, Luigi Rossi (has the title "Lamento di Cecco").
I Rc, 2475, ff. 179-210v, anon. (the last folio is badly torn).
A Wn, 18610, ff. 17v-28v, anon. (has the title "Lamento di Cecco").

B Bc, 12900, pp. 23-37 (copy of 18610).
Another setting for soprano solo:
I Rvat, Chigi Q VI 80, ff. 129v-140, anon. (Marco Marazzoli).

182.   Sparite dal core, speranze fallaci.

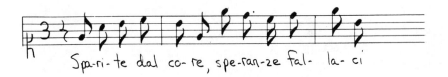

I Rsc, G 885, ff. 61-62v, Del d° (Luigi Rossi).

183.   Sparite dal volto, loquaci pallori. Gh. 223.

I Rvat, Barb. lat. 4208, ff. 105-108v, Luigi Rossi.

Between the 4th and the 5th measures of the musical incipit in Ghislanzoni's catalogue four measures are omitted.

184.   Sparsa il crine e lagrimosa dell'Egeo. Wo. 155, Gh. 234, Re. 97.

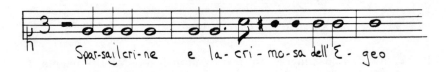

F Pn, Rés. Vm7 102, ff. 41-46v, Luigi Rossi, text by Fabio della Cornia.
(See below, no. 295.)

I Bc, Q 46, ff. 91v-94v, anon. (the attribution Luigi Rossi is a later addition in pencil). At the beginning of the piece is the title "Lamento di Zaida Mora."

I Rc, 2505, ff. 47-51, anon.

B Bc, 17192, pp. 40-49 (copy of Rés. Vm7 102).

185. Sparsa il crine, lagrimosa dell'Egeo. Gh. 234.

I Rvat, Chigi Q VII 99, ff. 7-10v, Luige Rossi, text by D. Fabio della Corgna (has the title "Lamento di Zaida Turca"). The text is the same as no. 184; the music is entirely different.

This version of *Sparsa il crine* is included among Luigi's oeuvre because there is no concordance that contests the attribution. However, I doubt this is Luigi's music.

186. Spenti gl'affanni ond'io perdei servendo, il fior degl'anni.

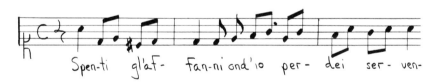

I Rc, 2480, ff. 191-192v, Del d° (Luigi Rossi).

187. Speranze, che dite, ancora credete che sete.

I Rsc, G 885, ff. 57-60v, del dᵒ (Luigi Rossi).
I Rc, 2505, ff. 95-97, anon.
F Pthibault, Rec. H.P. 31, pp. 163-167, anon.

—Stabat Mater

"Cantata del Cav. Marino sopra lo *Stabat Mater*, messa in musica dal medesimo Rossi."

I Fbn, Magl. XIX.22. The manuscript is lost. See below, no. 384.

188.   Su la veglia d'una speme il mio cor penando stà. Wo. 157, Gh. 240, Re. 98.

GB Ouf, MS U.210.4, ff. 1-6v, Luigi Rossi.
F Pthibault, G.T. 3, ff. 69-74v, Luigi Rossi.
I Rvat, Barb. lat. 4163, ff. 1-4v, Luigi.
I MOe, Mus. G 257, ff. 31-35, Luigi Rossi.
I Rvat, Barb. lat. 4208, ff. 109-111, anon.
B Bc, 17193, pp. 54-56 (copy of Mus. G 257).
P, pp. 12-14.

189.   Sù, consiglio, ò miei pensieri. Gh. 241.

I Rsc, G 885, ff. 29-36, Del dᵒ (Luigi Rossi).
I Rvat, Barb. lat. 4208, ff. 101v-104v, anon.

190.   Sù, sù, sù, mio core, la guerra! Un guardo guerriero ne sfida.

I Rbn, 71.9.A.33, ff. 99-102v, Luigi Rossi.
I Rvat, Barb. lat. 4203, ff. 51-64v, anon.

191.   Taci, ohimè, non pianger più, cor dolente. Wo. 158, Gh. 242, Re. 61.

F Pn, Rés. Vm7 59, ff. 115-116v, Luigi Rossi.
US CA, MS Mus 106, no. 32, ff. (107-108v), anon.
B Bc, F 664, pp. 67-70; 28072, pp. 68-71 (copies of Rés. Vm7 59).

192.   Tenti e ardisca in amore chi brama gioire.

I Rc, 2478, ff. 157-162v, Luigi.
I Nc, 33.4.19, ff. 33-38v, anon.
B Bc, F.A. VI 38, ff. 175-181v, anon.

193.   Torna indietro, pensier, dove si và. Wo. 160, Gh. 246.

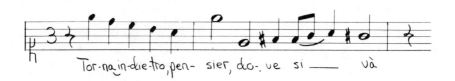

GB Och, 998, ff. 65-78v, Del dº (Luigi Rossi).
I Rvat, Barb. lat. 4168, ff. 34-38v, L.R. (lacks text of 3d strophe of final aria).
I Ria, MS. 1, ff. 44-52v (the present foliation does not account for the missing folios; the folios here are actually 47-55v since folios 23, 35, and 38 are missing), lacks text of 3d strophe of final aria, anon.

194.   Tra montagne di foco romito vive il core. Wo. 161, Gh. 250, Re. 42.

B Br, II 3947, ff. 99-102v, Luigi Rossi.
I Rc, 2479, ff. 1-4, anon.
I Rvat, Barb. lat. 4150, ff. 80-82v, anon.
I Rvat, Chigi Q IV 5, ff. 100v-101v, anon.
I Rc, 2505, ff. 103v-104v, anon.
B Bc, 17193, pp. 34-37 (copy of II 3947).
Eins, 87, 21-22 (copy of II 3947).

195.   Tra romite contrade, mesta il cor. Wo. 162, Gh. 251, Re. 99.

F Pn, Rés. Vm7 59, ff. 67-69v, Luigi Rossi, text by Antonio Abbati.
B Bc, 17192, pp. 178-183 (copy of Rés. Vm7 59).

196.   Tutto cinto di ferro e con più armi. Wo. 163, Gh. 254.

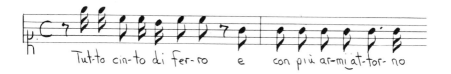

GB Och, 998, ff. 53-64v, Luigi Rossi (has the title "Lo sdegno smargasso").
I Rvat, Barb. lat. 4200, ff. 25v-33, anon.
Another version for soprano solo:
I Bc, Q 47, ff. 111-117, Carlo Caprioli, text by Francesco Melosi (has the
title "Lo sdegno smargiasso").

197.   Un cor che non chiede aita non speri trovar pietà. Wo. 164, Gh. 257.

GB Ouf, MS U.210.4, ff. 35-38, Luigi Rossi.
F Pn, Vm7 17, pp. 68-70, Luigi.
F Pn, Vm7 6, f. 17, Luigi Rossi.
B Bc, 15261, pp. 62-63 (copy of Vm7 6).
GB Och, 17, f. 26v, anon.

Ecorcheville, op. cit., VII, 190, incorrectly gives Vm7 3, p. 27, as a concordance. *Un cor che non chiede* is not in Vm7 3.

Another setting, for soprano, alto, and baritone:
I Bc, Q 44, ff. 202-204v, anon.
GB Lbm, Add. 31505, ff. 102-105v, anon.
D HV1, MS IV 422, pp. 31-32 (first soprano part only).

198. Un ferito cavaliero di polve, di sudor. Wo. 165, Gh. 258, Re. 100.

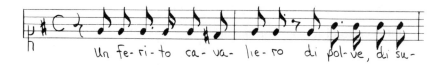

F Pn, Rés. Vm7 59, ff. 47-54v, Luigi Rossi, text by Fabio della Corgna.[14]
I Rvat, Chigi Q VII 99, ff. 11-16v, Luige Rossi, text by Fabio della Corgna (the text begins "Ferito un cavaliero").
I Rc, 2479, ff. 5-18v, Luigi Rossi (has the title "Lamento della Regina di Svetia"). Below the continuo line is a second text, not in any of the other sources—a "travestimento spirituale." It begins "Un allato messaggiero da pietà, da stupor." This added text, the attribution, and the title are not in the hand of the original text, but in a hand contemporary with it.
I Bc, Q 46, ff. 80-84v, anon. (the attribution Luigi Rossi is a later addition). The title "Lamento della Regina di Svetia" is at the beginning of the cantata.
I MOe, Mus. G 239, pp. 68-79, anon. (has the title "Cantata di Gustavo Adolfo Re di Svetia morto in guerra").
F Pthibault, Rec.H.P. 31, pp. 284-297 (the pages should be correctly numbered 264-277), anon.
B Bc, 17192, pp. 18-33 (copy of Rés. Vm7 59).
The first 22 measures are quoted by Antonio Francesco Tenaglia in his cantata *Che volete ch'io canti.*[15] I Nc, 33.4.17, II, 103-113v.

The composition dates after the death (lamented in the text) of Gustavus Adolphus II, King of Sweden, on Nov. 16, 1632, and before August, 1641, when Ottaviano Castelli sent a copy of the cantata from Rome to Cardinal Mazarin in Paris.[16] Ghislanzoni (p. 56) theorizes that the work was composed only after Mazarin's departure from Rome in 1639.

199. Un pensier nobile si mi ragiona tua fede immobile. Wo. 166, Gh. 259.

I Rvat, Barb. lat. 4173, ff. 77-78, Luigi.

200.   Uscite di porto, pensieri volanti.

I Rc, 2467, ff. 85v-91, Luigi.

A setting of a shortened version of the text, for soprano solo:
I Rvat, Chigi Q IV 80, ff. 117v-119, anon. (Marco Marazzoli).

201.   Vè, vè che miro? Io miro una fortuna.

I Rc, 2466, ff. 59-64v, Luigi (the attribution is not in the hand of the text,
   but in the hand of other texts in the manuscript, see above, no. 126,
   Non la volete intendere).
US CHH, Music Vault M2. 1 M1, ff. 50-53, anon.

202.   Voi siete troppo belle, o mie catene.

US LA, MS fC 697 M.4, pp. 4-6, Luigi Rossi.

D Mbs, 1524, ff. 116-118v, anon.
Another setting for soprano solo, see below, no. 407.

Duets

203.   Ahi, dunque è pur vero, anima del mio core. Gh. 265.
         For two sopranos and continuo.

I Fc, D 2357, ff. 155-157v, Luigi.

204.   Ahi, quante volte io moro e morendo vi chieggio. Gh. 266.
         For soprano, bass, and continuo.

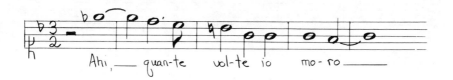

I Fc, D 2357, ff. 178v-180, Luigi (lacks the continuo part for 38 of the 77
measures).

205.   A i sospiri, al dolore a i tormenti, al penare.
         For two sopranos and continuo.

F Pthibault, Rec. H.P.2, ff. 57-72v, Luigi Rossi. (The music of the second strophe is a variation of that of the first.)

I Bc, Q 46, ff. 52-53v, anon. (The music of the first strophe is repeated for the second strophe.)

I Nc, 33.3.1, ff. 171-174 (first soprano), anon.; 33.3.2, I, 72-75 (second soprano), anon.; 33.3.2, II, 83-84 (basso continuo), anon.

206.   Amor, con dolci vezzi tu pur lusinghi il core. Gh. 268.
        For two sopranos and continuo.

I Fc, D 2357, ff. 61v-64, Luigi.
I Rc, 2480, ff. 303-312v, del d° (Luigi Rossi).
I Bc, Q 47, ff. 127v-130v, Carlo Caprioli.

207.   Amor, se devo piangere, voglio saper perche. Wo. 168, Gh. 269 and 306.
        For soprano, alto, and continuo.

GB Och, 996, ff. 131v-132v, Luigi Rossi.
I Fc, D 2357, ff. 171-172, Luigi.
B Bc, F 662, pp. 158-162, Luigi Rossi.
GB Och, 337, ff. 47v-49, anon.
Eins, 86, 14-15 (copy of F 662).
Ld, II, 83-85.

Mio cor, non ti difendere in the second strophe in all of the sources except D 2357 where the order of the strophes is reversed. Ghislanzoni, not realizing that the music of *Mio cor, non ti difendere* in D 2357 is the same music to which *Amor, se devo piangere* is set in the other sources, lists them as separate pieces.

208.   Apritevi, o begl'occhi, ne più chiusi tenete Gh. 270.
       For two sopranos and continuo.

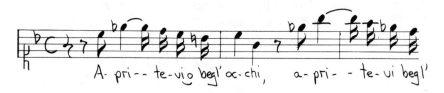

I Fc, D 2357, ff. 96-97, Luigi.

209.   Ardo, sospiro, e piango. Osservo eterna fè. Gh. 271.
       For two sopranos and continuo.

I Nc, 22.5.15, ff. 69-81v, Luiggi Rossi.
Another setting for soprano, baritone, and continuo:[17]
GB Och, 997, ff. 13-25v, Stradella.
GB Rc, R.C.M. 601, ff. 25-29v, Stradella.
I Bc, V 195, ff. 24v-27, anon.
D MUs, 4087, ff. 26-28v, anon.
I Nc, 22.1.4, ff. 22-31v, anon.

The version of the text set by Luigi has two quatrains omitted in the version set by Stradella. They are interpolated between the verses Stradella uses as a refrain and those he uses as the second strophe. The text set by Stradella ends with a strophe of five lines omitted in the version set by Luigi. In Stradella's setting the tercet following the first strophe is used as a refrain; in Luigi's setting it is not.

Yet another setting, for soprano, two violins, and continuo:
(Here the text is limited to two strophes, the first and last of Stradella's
setting.The fifth and sixth verses of the first strophe are used as a refrain
and return after the fourth verse of the last strophe. The fifth verse of the
last strophe is omitted so that the strophes are equal in length.)
I Vnm, and US Wc (negative photo copy of the Venetian MS), *L'Artemisia*,
opera composed by Francesco Cavalli, ff. 35v-38. The text is by Nicolo
Minato, and the first performance was at the theater of SS. Giovanni e
Paolo in Venice, in 1656.

If Luigi did compose the duet attributed to him in the Neapolitan MS, its
text existed before 1653, the year of Luigi's death, and is probably not
originally part of Minato's libretto.[18] Should it prove that this text does
originate in Minato's libretto, then, of course, the attribution to Luigi in
the Neapolitan MS is incorrect.

210.   A te, mio core, a te non ti fidar d'un ciglio, Wo. 169, Gh. 273.
        For soprano, alto, and continuo.

I Fc, D 2357, ff. 148-150, Luigi (in d minor).
I Bc, Q50, ff. 96v-98v, Luigi.
F Pn, Vm7 6, ff. 19r-19v, Luigi Rossi.
GB Och, 996, ff. 108bis-109, Luigi Rossi.
B Bc, F 662, pp. 134-137, Luigi Rossi.
I Rvat, Barb. lat. 4200, ff. 181v-185, anon.
Eins, 85, 105 (copy of 4200); 86, 11-12 (copy of F 662).
Ld, II, 66-69.

In all the sources the second voice is an alto, not a soprano as in Ghislanzoni's catalogue. The second voice part in the musical incipit given by
Ghislanzoni should be read transposed a fifth below.

211.   Augellin di sete acceso, io ti lascio in libertà. Gh. 274.
       For two sopranos and continuo.

I Fc, D 2357, ff 33v-38, Luigi.
Another setting, for soprano solo (see below, no. 303):
I Rvat, Barb. lat. 4200, ff. 37-38, anon.
I Rvat, Chigi, Q IV 8, ff. 36-37v, anon.
Yet another setting for soprano solo:
I Nc, 33.5.25, ff. 120-124, anon.

212.   Bella bocca tutta fiori, delle gratie degl'amori.
       For two sopranos and continuo.

I Rc, 2480, ff. 283-288, del d° (Luigi Rossi).
I Nc, 33.5.10, ff. 140-145, anon.
I Nc, 33.3.1, ff. 70-71 (first soprano), anon.; 33.3.2, I 18v-20 (second
   soprano), anon.; 33.3.2, II, 7v (basso continuo), anon.

213.   Che non puote sereno sguardo se diletta pur quando ancide.
       For two sopranos and continuo.

I Rc, 2480, ff. 275-282v, Luigi Rossi.

214. Che pretendete, begl'occhi, da me ch'io v'ami e v'adori. Wo. 170, Gh. 276.
      For two sopranos and continuo.

I Bc, Q 50, ff. 81-83, Luigi.
D Fc, D 2357, ff. 59-61, Luigi.
I Rc, 2466, ff. 233-242, Luigi Rossi.
I Bc, Q 44 ff. 42v-45v, anon.
I Nc, 33.4.14, ff. 65-86, anon.
I Nc, 33.5.10, ff. 112-115, anon.
I Nc, 33.3.1, ff. 123v-125 (first soprano); 33.3.2, I, 44v-46 (second soprano), anon.; 33.3.2, II, 47-48b (basso continuo), anon.
US CHH, Music Vault M2. 1 M1, ff. 161v-164, anon.

215. Che sospiri, martiri, che dolori, che pianti! Gh. 277.
      For two sopranos and continuo.

I Fc, D 2357, ff. 113v-114, Luigi.

216.   Chi d'amor sin'à i capelli dentro al mar se stesso. Gh. 278.
         For two sopranos and continuo.

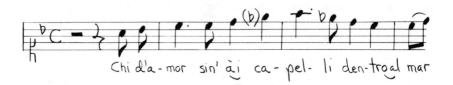

Chi d'a-mor sin'à i ca-pel- li den-tro al mar

I Fc, D 2357, ff. 146v-147v, Luigi.

217.   Chi d'amor sin'à i capelli dentro al mar se stesso.
         For two sopranos and continuo.

Chi d'amor sin'à i ca — pel — li

I Bc, V/289, ff. 257-260v, del dᵒ (Luigi Rossi), text by Monsignore Vai.
I Bc, Q 48, ff. 99v-101, anon.

Both settings have a second strophe, but the texts are not the same. The second strophe for the setting in D 2357 begins "Nel medesimo momento," while the second strophe in Q 48 begins "Chi si strugge e serve a Donna."

218.   Chi non sà com'un sol sguardo privi il cor di libertà. Gh. 279.
         For soprano, baritone, and continuo.

Chi non sà com'— un sol guar-do —

I Fc, D 2357, ff. 89-94, Luigi.

I Bc, V 195, ff. 22-23, anon.
I Bsp, Lib. S.13-II (copy of V 195).
GB Rc, R.C.M. 601, ff. 15v-17, Stradella.

The attribution of the twenty-three duets in this eighteenth-century manuscript is at the beginning of the volume in the title "Duetti, Terzetti, del Sig. Stradella." This title, in the hand of the copyist, implies that the pieces were carefully assembled. In collections such as this, in which a special effort was made to assemble pieces by one composer, the attributions are usually quite certain. Nevertheless, it is the writer's opinion that the two duets *Chi non sà* and *Soffrirei con lieto core* are Luigi Rossi's because the attributions Luigi and Luigi Rossi of the two duets in four other manuscripts are no less reliable than the attribution Stradella. In addition, the list of works which over the centuries have been attributed to the romantic figure of Alessandro Stradella is remarkable for its many spurious inclusions.

219. Chi può resister, chi? Troppo forti guerrieri. Wo. 171, Gh. 281.
     For two sopranos and continuo.

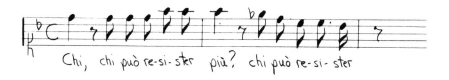

I Bc, Q 50, ff. 49-51v, Luigi.
I Nc, 33.4.13, ff. 65-72v, Luigi Rossi.
I Nc, 33.5.10, ff. 190-193v, anon.
I Nc, 33.3.1, ff. 127-129v (first soprano) anon.; 33.3.2., I, 14v-16v (second soprano), anon.; 33.3.2, II, 50-52 (basso continuo), anon.

220. Come sete importuni, amorosi pensier! Privo d'ogni pietade. Gh. 282.
     For soprano, baritone, and continuo.

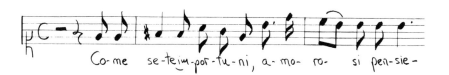

I D 2357, ff. 177-178, Luigi (lacks text of 2d strophe, but has the text of
the 3d strophe designated as "2a stanza").
Another setting for soprano solo:
I MOe, Mus. G 33, Carissimi, text by Benigni.
I Bc, V/289, ff. 153-156v, Iacomo Carissimi, text by Domenico Benigni.
US CA, MS Mus 106, no. 21, ff. (76-78v), anon.
Yet another setting for soprano solo:
US SFdeBellis, MS Misc. V.LXIX, ff. 54v-60, anon.

221.   Compatite un cor di foco che nel giaccio sta sepolto. Gh. 283.
       For soprano, bass, and continuo.

I Fc, D 2357, ff. 17-19, Luigi.

222.   Corilla danzando sul prato si stà; e l'aura scherzando. Gh. 284.
       For two sopranos and continuo.

I Fc, D 2357, ff. 114v-116v, Luigi.
Another version, a trio for soprano, alto, tenor, and continuo (not a quartet, as Ghislanzoni indicates):
I Fbn, and Bc, *Primo libro d'arie . . . Di Girolamo Frescobaldi* (Firenze,
1630), pp. 44-45.

223. Datemi pace una brev'hora almeno. Wo. 172, Gh. 286.
For soprano, mezzo-soprano, and continuo. (Vm 7 6 has the rubric "cum organo").

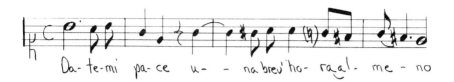

I Rvat, Chigi Q IV 16, ff. 137-148v, Luigi Rossi.
F Pn, Vm7 6, f. 20 (not p. 120, as Ghislanzoni indicates), Luigi Rossi.
GB Och, 996, ff. 112-113, Luigi Rossi, (lacks text of 2d strophe).
B Bc, 15261, pp. 22-23 (copy of Vm7 6).
US Wc, *Ariette di Musica* . . . (Bracciano, 1646), pp. 83-92, Luigi Rossi,
    Musico dell'Eminentiss. Card. Antonio Barberino.

(The lower voice is not an alto, as indicated in the previous catalogues,
but a mezzo-soprano.)

224. Di capo ad'Amarilli solo per mio tormento. Gh. 287.
For two sopranos and continuo.

I Fc, D 2357, ff. 158-159v, Luigi.

225. Dite, o cieli, se crudeli sono i sguardi. Wo. 173, Gh. 288.
For soprano, bass or baritone (in some of the sources the lower
voice is a bass; in others, a baritone), and continuo.

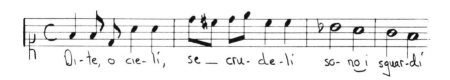

I Rvat, Chigi Q IV 16, ff. 91-96v, Luigi Rossi.
F Pn, Vm7 4, pp. 8-13, Luigi.
GB Lbm, Harl. 1501, ff. 69-69v, Luigi Rossi (lacks continuo).
D SW, 4718a, pp. 32-34, Luigi.
GB Rc, R.C.M. 1102, ff. 54v-55, Louigi Rossi (lacks continuo).
D SW, 4718b, pp. 103-105, anon.
D MÜs, 4087, ff. 8v-10, anon.
GB Och, 337, ff. 33v-35, anon. (the attribution Rossi is a later addition in pencil).
I Nc, 33.5.10, ff. 206-209, anon.
F Pc, H 659, II, 218-223, anon.
GB Lbm, Add. 31461, ff. 83v ff., anon.; Add. 33235, ff. 46v-52v, anon.; Add. 29397, ff. 88v-83v (reversing the MS), anon. (the attribution Carissimi is a later addition); Add. 31455, part III, f. 27v, and part IV, f. 61 (bass and continuo parts), anon.
GB Ob, Mus.Sch.E 393, ff. 31v-32, anon. First stanza only.
GB Lwa, CG 63, p. 266, anon. First stanza only (lacks continuo).
GB Lwa, CG 27, pp. 80-81, anon. First stanza only (lacks continuo).
GB Bu, 5002, p. 241, anon. (lacks continuo).
GB Lam, 107, p. 112, Carissimi. First stanza only (continuo added by a different hand).
GB Lbm, Add. 31817, f. 10v, Carissimi, with the comment "From Dr. Phil Hayes's MS."
A Wn, 17034, ff. 6-7, Carissimi.

Printed in Sir John Hawkins, *A General History . . . of Music* (London, 1776), 789-790, Carissimi (first strophe).
B Bc, XY 8283, *Recueil des meilleurs airs italiens . . .* (Paris: Christophe Ballard 1708), II, 134-136, Luiggi.
US NYp, Drexel 4157, *Banquet of Music . . .* (London: Henry Playford 1688), II, 22-23, anon.
Further printed sources:
Recueil des meilleurs air italiens . . . (Paris, 1703 and 1705), pp. 134-136, Luiggi.
Apollonian Harmony, II, 30-31, Carissimi.

The text of the second strophe is missing in most of the sources, but MSS 33.5.10, Q IV 16, and 4087 give it.

226. Due feroci guerrieri, cieco amor, a mia ruina. Gh. 290.
      For two sopranos and continuo.

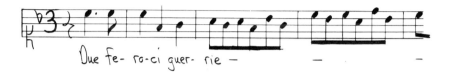

I Fc, D 2357, ff. 100v-103v, Luigi.

227. Due labbra di rose fan guerra al mio core. Wo. 174, Gh. 289. Re.
      44.
      For two sopranos and continuo.

I Fc, D 2357, ff. 49v-51v, Luigi.
I Nc, 22.5.15, ff. 49-51, Luiggi Rossi.
I Bc, Q 44, ff. 162-165, del medesmo (Luigi Rossi).
I Rc, 2464, ff. 31-38, Luigi Rossi.
I Rc, 2480, ff. 289-296v, del d° (Luigi Rossi).
F Pn, Vm7 53, pp. 82-84, Luigi. (The voice parts are written on treble
  staves; the tonality is C major.)
GB Ob, Mus. Sch.E 393, ff. 25v-27, anon.
F Pc, H 659, II, 194-200, anon.
B Bc, 17193, pp. 5-9 (copy of Q 44).
B Bc, XY 8283, *Recueil des meilleurs airs italiens* . . . (Paris, Christophe
  Ballard, 1708), III, 205-210, anon. (the attribution Luigi Rossi is a later
  addition).
T, V, 190 ff.

228.   E che pensi, mio core, con tanto dir no. Gh. 291.
        For two sopranos and continuo.

I Nc, 33.4.13, ff. 91-104, Luigi Rossi.
F Pthibault, Rec. H.P. 5, ff. 149-164, anon.
I Nc, 33.5.10, ff. 182-189, anon.
I Nc, 33.3.1, ff. 87-90v (first soprano), anon.; 33.3.2, II, 21v-23 (basso continuo), anon.

229.   Filli, non penso più a destarti nel sen fiamma d'amore. Gh. 292.
        For soprano, bass, and continuo.

I Fc, D 2357, ff. 108v-111, Luigi; a second copy on ff. 180v-183, Luigi.

230.   Frena il pianto, ahi, non più no, lacrimar. Gh. 293.
        For soprano, alto, and continuo.

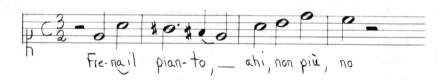

I Fc, D 2357, ff. 124-125v, Luigi.

231. Guardate dove và la mia vana speranza. Gh. 294.
For two sopranos and continuo.

Guar-da-te _ do- ve _ và la mia va- na spe- ran –

I Fc, 2357, ff. 38v-40v, Luigi.

232. Ha cent'occhi il crudo amore se ben cieco altri lo pinge. Gh. 295.
For two sopranos and continuo.

Ha cent'oc-chi il cru-do a-mo-re   se ben cie-co al –

I Fc, D 2357, ff. 105v-106v, Luigi.
I Nc, Q 48, ff. 181v-183v, anon.
I Rc, 2464, ff. 64-67v, anon.

233. Ho perso il mio core e chi con frode rapito me l'ha. Gh. 296.
For two sopranos and continuo.

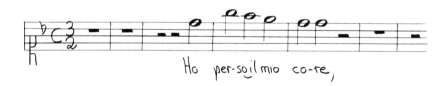

Ho per-so il mio co-re,

I Fc, D 2357, ff. 119-121, Luigi.

—Hora mi lusinga più. Gh. 297.

See Non mi lusingar più speranza infida, no. 240, below.

234. Il contento che mi deste nel mirarmi, o luci belle. Wo. 175, Gh.
      298.
      For soprano, mezzo-soprano, and continuo.

Il con-ten- to __ che_ mi de- sta nel

I Nc, 33.4.13, ff. 123-128v, Luigi Rossi.
GB Och, 996, ff. 125-126, Luigi Rossi.
B Bc, F 662, pp. 169-174, Luigi Rossi.
Eins, 86, 15-16 (copy of F 662).

235. Infelice pensier, chi ne conforta, ohimè. Wo. 81, Gh. 117.
      For two sopranos and continuo.

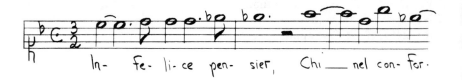

In- fe- li-ce pen- sier, Chi __ nel con- for-

I Bc, Q 50, ff. 90v-96, Luigi.
Ld, II, 86-92, the duet *Dite, o Pensier*.

(Both Wotquenne and Ghislanzoni erroneously list *Infelice pensier* with
the solo pieces. It is a duet and dialogue for two sopranos, "Pensiero"
and "Amante.")

236.   Invan mi tendete il visco e la rete, fallaci detti. Gh. 299.
For two sopranos and continuo.

I Fc, D 2357, ff. 104-105, Luigi.

237.   Libertà, ragion mi sgrida; servitù, mi dice amore. Wo. 176, Gh.
301.
For two sopranos and continuo.

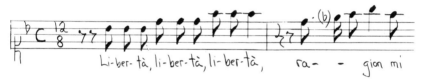

I Bc, Q 50, ff. 15-16v, Luigi.
I Rc, 2464, ff. 72-77v, anon.

238.   Lo splendor di due begl'occhi, di due labbra l'armonia. Wo. 177,
Gh. 302.
For two sopranos and continuo.

I Bc, Q 47, ff. 155-164, Luigi Rossi.
I Fc, D 2357, ff. 41-49, Luigi.
I Rc, 2464, ff. 78-95v, Luigi Rossi.
GB Lbm, Add. 31505, ff. 20-39, anon.

Va, Serie I, no. 1, the solo aria *No pensier, non mi rispondere*.

—Mio cor, non ti difendere se vuoi trovar pietà. Gh. 306.

See Amor, se devo piangere, voglio saper perchè, no. 207, above.

239.   Non cantar libertà, misero core, che sciolto non sei tu. Wo. 178, Gh. 307.
    For soprano, baritone, and continuo.

GB Och, 996, ff. 109v-110, Luigi Rossi.
I Rvat, Chigi Q IV 16, ff. 27-30v, Luigi Rossi.

240.   Non mi lusingar più, speranza infida. Wo. 179, Gh. 297 and 310.
    For soprano, alto, and continuo.

I Bc, Q 50, ff. 53v-55, Luigi.
I Nc, 33.4.13, ff. 51-56v, Luigi Rossi.
I Nc, 33.3.1, ff. 125v-127 (first soprano), anon. 33.3.2, II, 48v-50 (basso continuo), anon.
GB Lbm, Add. 31816, ff. 135v ff. R.J.S. Stevens, transcriber of the volume, attributes the duet to Agostino Steffani. Einstein, in his short description of this MS, *DTB*, VI^2, p. xvi, remarks that the last duet in the MS, *Fermatevi folli pensieri,* is by a composer of the Roman school, and that the two which precede it (*Non mi lusingar* and *Pene, che volete*) are by Luigi Rossi.

A setting of a considerably longer version of the text, for soprano solo:
I Rc, 2478, ff. 60-69v, Marc'Ant° Pasqualini.
I Rvat, Barb. lat. 4223, ff. 106-109v, MAP.

Einstein, "Collection . . . ," op. cit., 85, 39, errs in identifying the text
of the duet *Non mi lusingar più cieco mondo fallace*, by Gio. Batt. Maz-
zaferrata, with the text of the duet set by Luigi.

241. Non più strali, amor, non più. Gh. 312.
      Non più strali, o crudo amore, il mio sen trafitto giace.
      For soprano, baritone, and continuo.

I Fc, D 2357, ff. 175-176v, Luigi.
(The lower voice is a baritone, not a bass, as Ghislanzoni indicates.)

Ghislanzoni gives the first incipit, the words as they occur below the
soprano part. Restoring the text to its original form, one obtains the
second incipit.

242. O biondi tesori inanellati chiome di mille cori laberinti. Gh. 314.
      For two sopranos and continuo.

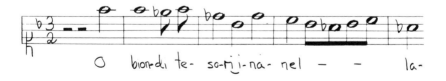

I Fc, D 2357, ff. 71v-73, Luigi.
US CHH, Music Vault M2. 1 M1, ff. 144-149, anon.

243.   Occhi belli, occhi miei cari, raffrenate il vostro sguardo. Wo. 180,
       Gh. 315.
       The two voice parts are written on treble staves.

F Pn, Vm7 53, pp. 70-73, Luigi.
B Bc, 15261, pp. 28-31 (copy of Vm7 53).

Ghislanzoni gives F Pn, Vm7 1, p. 30 as a concordance, but the duet is
nowhere in this MS.

244.   Occhi, quei vaghi azuri onde l'haveste. Wo. 181, Gh. 318, Re. 45.
       For soprano, bass, and continuo.

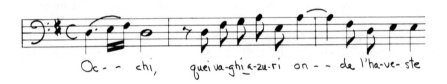

GB Cfm, 24.F.4, ff. 95-96v, Luigi Rossi.
GB Lbm, Harl. 1863, ff. 4v-8, anon.
B Bc, 17193, pp. 207-212 (copy of 24.F.4).

245.   Occhi soavi ogn'aspro cor a intenerir. Gh. 319.
       For two sopranos and continuo.

I Fc, D 2357, ff. 160-161v, Luigi.

246.   O cieli, pietà, e l'alma svanita. Wo. 182, Gh. 320.
       For two sopranos and continuo.

GB Och, 996, ff. 119v-120v, Luigi Rossi.
GB Lbm, Harl. 1863, ff. 11v-13, Luigi Rossi (lacks texts of 2d and 3d
    strophes).
B Bc, F 662, pp. 142-146, Luigi Rossi.
GB Och, 377, ff. 27v-30, anon. (lacks texts of 2d and 3d strophes).
Eins, 86, 12-13 (copy of F 662).

247.   O gradita libertà, oh beata servitù. Gh. 366.
       For soprano, tenor, and continuo.

I Nc, 22.5.15, ff. 83, Luiggi Rossi.
I Nc, 60.1.50, ff. 71-93v, anon.

248.   Pene, che volete da me? Wo. 184, Gh. 323.
       Pene, pianti e sospiri, che volete da me?
       For soprano, bass, and continuo.

P La, 47-II-1, ff. 85-90v, Luigi Rossi.
GB Och, 996, ff. 114v-115, Luigi Rossi.
GB Lbm, Harl. 1501, ff. 5-6, Luiggi Rossi.
I Rvat, Chigi Q IV 16, ff. 31-40, Luigi Rossi.
GB Och, 377, ff. 40v-43, anon. (the attribution Rossi is a later addition in pencil).
D MÜs, 4087, ff. 19-20, anon. (lacks continuo).
GB Lbm, Add. 31816, ff. 133v ff., Agostini Steffani (concerning the attribution, see *Non mi lusingar*, no. 240).
Catalogo della Aire, . . . *in manoscritto nella Officina Musica di G. G. I. Breitkopf* (Leipzig, 1765), Parte VIta, p. 35, Rossi. Only the first two measures of the soprano part are given. The MS to which the catalogue refers is unknown to the writer.

The first text incipit is given in the Wotquenne and Ghislanzoni catalogues. It is taken from the first soprano's first and second phrases. Between the two, the bass interjects the words "pianti e sospiri." Texts beginning with a series of three nouns, interjections, or verbs are common, e.g.: *O grotta, o speco, o sasso; Pianti, pene, sospiri; Ardo, sospiro e piango; Prega, sospira e plora; Olà, olà, olà pensieri*, and *Piango, prego e sospiro*.

249.   Pietà, spietati lumi, non ti chieggio più. Wo. 185, Gh. 328.
    For soprano, baritone, and continuo.

P La, 47-II-1, ff. 81-84, Luigi Rossi.
GB Lbm, Harl. 1863, ff. 153v-156v, Luigi.
GB Och, 377, ff. 51v-53, anon. (The lower voice is a baritone. The tonality is e minor.)
GB Lbm, Add. 14336, ff. 16v-17v, anon. (mistakenly listed as a source with attribution in Ghislanzoni's catalogue).
B Bc, 17197, pp. 131-133 (copy of Harl. 1863).

250.   Poiche mancò speranza che mi nutriva il cor. Wo. 186, Gh. 330.
        For two sopranos and continuo.

GB Och, 996, ff. 121-124v, Luigi Rossi.
I Fc, D 2357, ff. 54-56v, Luigi.
B Bc, F 662, pp. 174-179, Luigi Rossi.
Both Wotquenne and Ghislanzoni give I Bc, *D'Autori romani . . . libro III* (Q 46) as an anonymous concordance, but the writer has not found *Poiche mancò speranza* in any of the MSS in the Bologna library.
Eins, 86, 16-17 (copy of F 662).
Ld, II, 70-74.

251.   Provai d'amor le pene, hor non più, nò. Gh. 331.
        For two sopranos and continuo.

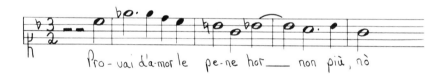

I Fc, D 2357, ff. 107-108, Luigi.

252.   Queste dure catene che strascinar lunga stagione. Wo. 187, Gh. 334.
        For soprano, baritone, and continuo.

I Fc, D 2357, ff. 183-184v, Luigi.
GB Och, 996, ff. 113v-114, Luigi Rossi.

253.   Risolvetevi, o martiri, di dar tregua al mio dolore. Wo. 188, Gh.
        335.
        For soprano, alto, and continuo.

GB Och, 996, ff. 110v-111v, Luigi Rossi.
I Rvat, Chigi Q IV 16, ff. 97-102v, Luigi Rossi.

254.   Sempre, dunque, negarete, belle ninfe, a noi mercè.
        For two sopranos and continuo.

I Rc, 2464, ff. 180-183v, Luigi Rossi.

255.   Si o nò, dissi al mio core. Nò, ripose. Wo. 189, Gh. 337.
        For two sopranos and continuo.

I Bc, Q 50, ff. 79-80v, Luigi.

I Nc, 33.4.13, ff. 57-64v, Luigi Rossi.
I Rc, 2464, ff. 218-223v, anon.
I Nc, 33.3.1, ff. 79v-81 (first soprano), anon.; 33.3.2, II, 16v-17 (basso continuo), anon.
GB Lbm, Add. 31505, ff. 2-5v, anon.
Ld, II, 75-78.

256.   Soffrirei con lieto core i martiri ch'ho nel seno. Wo. 190, Gh. 338. For soprano, baritone (except in MS F 662, where the lower voice is a bass), and continuo.

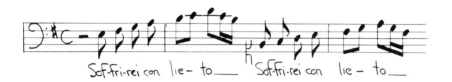

P La, 47-II-1, ff. 71-74v, Luigi Rossi.
GB Och, 996, ff. 126v-127v, Luigi Rossi.
I Rvat, Chigi Q IV 16, ff. 19-26v, Luigi Rossi.
B Bc, F 662, pp. 147-150, Luigi Rossi.
I Bc, V 195, ff. 20v-21v, anon.
I Bsp, Lib. S. 13-II (copy of V 195).
GB Rc, R.C.M. 601, ff. 12v-15v, Stradella. Concerning the attribution see *Chi non sa com'un sol sguardo*, no.218, above.
Eins, 86, 13-14 (copy of F 662).

257.   Speranza, al tuo pallore si che non speri. Wo. 191, Gh. 339. For two sopranos and continuo.

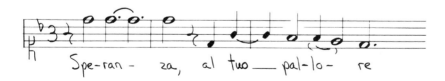

I Bc, Q 50, ff. 55v-56v, Luigi.
Ld, II, 79-92.

258.   Speranze, sentite, vi chiama anche amore. Gh. 340.
        For two sopranos and continuo.

I Nc, 33.4.13, ff. 73-80v, Luigi Rossi.
I Nc, 33.3.1, ff. 92v-93v (first soprano), anon.; 33.3.2, I 46v-49v (second
    soprano), 33.3.2, II 25-27 (basso continuo), anon.
I Nc, 33.5.10, ff. 30-33v, anon.
F Pthibault, Rec.H.P.5, ff. 42v-46, anon.

259.   Spiega un volo così altero l'alta mia speme. Wo. 192, Gh. 341, Re.
        47.
        For soprano, bass or baritone (in some of the MSS the lower part
        is notated on the bass staff; in others, on the baritone staff), and
        continuo.

P La, 47-II-1, ff. 99-102v, Luigi Rossi.
I Fc, D 2357, ff. 185-186v, Luigi.
I Rvat, Chigi Q IV 16, ff. 11-18v, Luigi Rossi.
GB Och, 996, ff. 118-119, Luigi Rossi.
GB Lbm, Harl. 1501, ff. 9-10v, Luiggi Rossi.
GB Lbm, Harl. 1863, ff. 1v-4v, Luiggi Rossi.
B Bc, 17197, p. 113 (copy by Wotquenne of the Harley MSS.)

260. Tu giuri ch'è mio quel seno che vedo. Wo. 193, Gh. 342.
For soprano, baritone (in MS Harl. 1501 only is the lower voice a bass), and continuo.

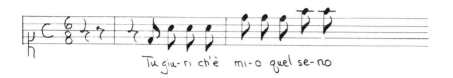

GB Lbm, Harl. 1501, ff. 10v-12, Luigi Rossi.
GB Och, 996, ff. 115v-116v, Luigi Rossi.
I Nc, 33.5.10, ff. 236-241, anon.
B Bc, 15258, pp. 17-19 (copy of Harl. 1501).

Wotquenne and Ghislanzoni erroneously give I Rvat, Barb. lat. 4200, ff. 50v-52v as an anonymous concordance; it is actually another setting of the same text, for solo soprano. Ghislanzoni lists it again separately under the solos this time without identifying it with the duet version. See below, no. 398.

261. Tu sarai sempre il mio bene, la mia vita. Wo. 194, Gh. 343, Re. 43.
For two sopranos and continuo.

I Bc, V/289, ff. 237-240v, Luigi Rossi.
I Moe, Mus.G 171, Luiggi Rossi, text by Pannesio.
GB Lbm, 1501, ff. 3-4v, Luiggi Rossi.
GB Lbm, 1863, ff. 8v-11, Luiggi Rossi.
I Fc, D 2357, ff. 99-100, Luigi.
GB Och, 377, ff. 6v-10, anon. (the attribution Luigi Rossi is a later addition in pencil).
B Bc, 17193, pp. 88-90 (copy of Mus.G 171).
Eins, 85, 12 (copy of Mus. G 171).

All sources except Mus.G 171 lack the text of the 2d strophe.

262.   Un amante sen' viene à morir di dolore. Gh. 344.
        For soprano, alto, and continuo.

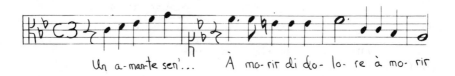

I Rvat, Chigi Q IV 16, ff. 87-90v, Luigi Rossi.

263.   Un tiranno di foco, uma furia di gelo. Gh. 345.
        For soprano, alto, and continuo.

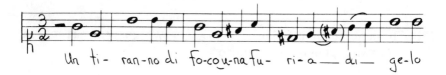

I Fc, D 2357, ff. 162-165v, Luigi.

264.   Viemmi, o sdegno, a difendere qual m'hai difeso già. Gh. 346.
        For two sopranos and continuo.

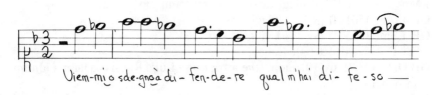

I Fc, D 2357, ff. 116v-117v, Luigi.

(The incipit Ghislanzoni gives begins "Vienmi" instead of "Viemmi," probably because "vienmi" shows the root of the verb more clearly; the text, however, has "Viemmi.")

265.   Vorrei scoprirti un dì con la piaga nel cor. Wo. 195, Gh. 347.
    For two sopranos and continuo.

I Fc, D 2357, ff. 121v-123v, Luigi.
GB Lbm, Harl. 1501, ff. 1-2v, Luiggi Rossi.
GB Lbm, Harl. 1863, ff. 20v-23v, Luiggi Rossi.
F Pn, Vm7 53, pp. 105-107, Luigi.
F Pn, Vm7 4, pp. 52-65, Luigi. (The F clef of the continuo staff is on the 4th line, but the notes are written as if it were on the 3d line.)
GB Rc, R.C.M. 2054, ff. 109v-112v, anon, (the attribution Louigi Rossi is a later attribution in pencil).
GB Och, 377, ff. 1-4, anon. (the attribution Rossi is a later addition in pencil).
GB Ob, Mus. Sch. E 393, ff. 14-16, anon.
D Sw, 4718b, pp. 111-116, anon.
I Rc, 2464, ff. 228-231, Carlo del Violino.
B Bc, XY 8283, *Recueil des meilleurs airs italiens* . . . (Paris: Christophe Ballard, 1708), II, 170-178, anon. (The attribution Luigi Rossi is a later addition.) In this source only, the duet is preceded by a three-part instrumental prelude.
Catalogo delle Arie. . . . in manoscritto nella Officina Musica di G. G. I. Breitkopf (Leipzig, 1765), Parte VIta, p. 35, anon. Only the first few notes of the first soprano part are given. The MS to which the catalogue refers is unknown to the writer.

The duet is in B-flat major in all of the sources except R.C.M. 2054, 4718b, Sch.E 393, and Harl. 1863, where it is in G major. The two voice parts are written on treble staves in the *Recueil* and in Vm7 4 and

Harl. 1501. The upper voice only is written on the treble staff in Vm7 53. Soprano staves are used in the other sources.

Trios

266.   Al bel lume d'un bel volto questo core il volo affretta. Wo. 196, Gh. 348, Re. 48.
        For three sopranos and continuo.
        (2d sop.)

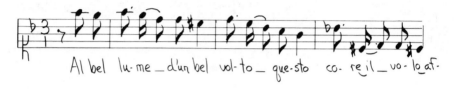

I Bc, Q 44, ff. 40-42v, Luigi Rossi.
I Rvat, Barb. lat. 4204, ff. 162v-164, anon. (lacks continuo for the first section).
B Bc, 17193, pp. 2-5 (copy of Q 44).
T, V, 186-189.

267.   Al far del dì per saper che facea la Donna bella. Wo. 197, Gh. 349.
        For two sopranos, tenor, and continuo.

GB Och, 996, ff. 130-131, Luigi Rossi.
B Bc, F 662, pp. 180-183, Luigi Rossi.

268. Amanti, ardire o goder o morire che penare e tacere. Wo. 198, Gh.
      350.
      For soprano, alto, baritone (the lowest voice is written in the bass
      clef in MS F 662 only) and continuo (the part is omitted after the
      entry of the baritone in the 4th measure; no doubt the continuo
      player followed the lowest voice part).

GB Och, 996, ff. 85v-87, Luigi Rossi.
B Bc, F 662, pp. 64-68, Luigi Rossi.
GB Och, 377, ff. 49v-51, anon.
D HVl, MS IV 422, pp. 33-34, anon. (the first soprano part only).

269. Deh, perchè non m'uccide il dolor del partire. Wo. 199, Gh. 351.
      For soprano, alto, and baritone (the lowest part is notated on the
      bass staff in MS F 622 only). There is no continuo part in any of
      the sources.

GB Och, 996, ff. 105v-107, Luigi Rossi.
B Bc, F 662, pp. 125-128, Luigi Rossi.
I Rvat, Barb. lat. 4200, ff. 121v-124, anon.
D HVl, MS IV 422, pp. 11-13, anon. (the first soprano part only).

270.   Di desire in desire portar, lasso, mi sento. Wo. 200, Gh. 352.
        For soprano, alto, baritone (the lowest voice is notated on the bass
        staff in MS F 662 only), and continuo.

GB Och, 996, ff. 81v-83, Luigi Rossi.
B Bc, F 662, pp. 50-56, Luigi Rossi.
GB Lbm, Add. 31505, ff. 177-180v, anon.

271.   Disperate speranze, a Dio, a Dio, se la bella ch'adoro. Wo. 201,
        Gh. 353.
        For three sopranos and continuo.

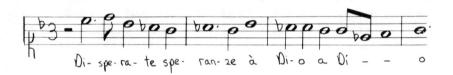

I Bc, Q 50, ff. 46v-48v, Luigi.
I Rvat, Barb. lat. 4200, ff. 145-150v, anon.

272.   Dolenti pensier miei, datevi pace. Wo. 202, Gh. 354.
        For soprano, alto, bass, and continuo.

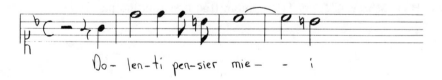

GB Och, 996, ff. 139-142, Luigi Rossi.
B Bc, F 662, pp. 163-168, Luigi Rossi.

GB Lbm, Add. 31505, ff. 74-81v, anon.

I Rvat, Chigi Q VI 85, ff. 68-71, anon. (lacks alto part, and is generally in an incomplete and defective state).

S Uu, Vok. mus. i. hs. 11:9, the bass part, two copies of the continuo, and an organ tablature of all of the parts for the first strophe. The attribution is Carissimi.

Another setting, for soprano solo:

I MOe, Campori, Y.L.11.9, ff. 114-118v, Giacomo Carissimi.

—D'una bella infedele ch'ha di spirto.

See *D'una bella infedele ch'ha di spirto*, no. 65, above.

273. Fan battaglia i miei pensieri ed al cor dan fiero assalto. Wo. 203, Gh. 355.

For three sopranos and continuo.

I Bc, Q 50, ff. 86-90, Luigi, text by Carlo C . . . aschi (?) (The script is small and unclear.)

274. Horche in notturna pace il mio bel sol riposa. Wo. 210, Gh. 367.

For soprano, alto, bass, and continuo.

GB Och, 996, ff. 73v-77, Luigi Rossi.

I Bc, Q 50, ff. 105-109, Luigi.

I Nc, 32.2.4, ff. 121-127v, Luiggi Rossi.

B Bc, F 662, pp. 24-36, Luigi Rossi (has the title "Serenata").
D HV1, MS IV 422, pp. 6-10, anon. (first soprano only).
I Nc, 22.1.2, a detached fascicle of eight unnumbered pages, anon. (the lowest voice is a baritone).
Eins, 86, 6-8 (copy of F 662).
Va, Serie I, no. 4, the trio "Dormite, begli occhi."

The second solo, a recitative for soprano in MSS 662, 32.2.4, 22.1.2, and 996, is replaced by a bass aria in MS Q 50. This MS differs also at the end of the first solo, in the second section of the first trio, and in the final trio, the last two verses.

275.   Horche notte guerriera d'ombre e d'orrori armata. Wo. 211, Gh. 368. Re. 5.
    For two sopranos ("Fortuna" and "Amore") and a tenor ("Amante"). The cantata begins with a Sinfonia for two violins and continuo.

I Bc, Q 46, ff. 139v-147, Luigi Rossi (has the title "Serenata").
B Bc, 17193, pp. 72-86 (copy of Q 46).
Va, Serie I, no. 2, the solo "Hor che notte" and no. 3, the trio "Di pur dunque."

(Opening Sinfonia)

276. In questo duro esiglio chieggio al mio proprio core. Wo. 204, Gh. 356.
For two sopranos, bass, and continuo.

P La, 47-I-65, ff. 19-22v, Luigi Rossi.
GB Och, 996, ff. 98v-100v, Luigi Rossi.
B Bc, F 662, pp. 106-112, Luigi Rossi.
GB Lbm, Add. 31505, ff. 82-86v, anon. (In the upper margin of f. 82, in a small hand, is an English text beginning "In vain I sigh." It may have served as a substitute text.)

277. Io mi glorio d'esser amante bench'ogn'hor voi mi ferite. Gh. 357.
For two sopranos, bass, and continuo.

I Nc, 33.2.4, ff. 28v-31v, Luiggi Rossi.
I Bc, Q 48, ff. 126-129, anon.
Another version, for soprano solo:
F Pc, Rés. 2095, ff. 3v-5, anon.

—Lasciate ch'io peni, dolenti pensieri. Gh. 359 and 377.

This trio is part of the complex *Il Peccator Pentito*. See Ghislanzoni, p. 112.

278. Lasso, benche mi fugga ogn'hor lontano. Wo. 205, Gh. 360.
     For soprano, alto, bass, and continuo.

GB Och, 996, ff. 83v-85, Luigi Rossi.
B Bc, F 662, pp. 57-63, Luigi Rossi.
GB Och, 377, ff. 53-56v, anon. (lacks continuo in some places).
GB Lbm, Add. 31505, ff. 181-187v, anon.

279. Mio cor, di che paventi? Soffri costante pene. Wo. 206, Gh. 361.
     For two sopranos, tenor, and continuo.

GB Och, 996, ff. 77v-79, Luigi Rossi (lacks continuo for the trio sections).
B Bc, F 662, pp. 36-43, Luigi Rossi.
GB Lbm, Add. 31505, ff. 168-172v, anon.
Eins, 86, 8-9 (copy of F 662).

280. Mio core, impara dal mare a piangere il tuo tormento. Wo. 207,
     Gh. 362.
     For soprano, alto, baritone (the lowest voice is a bass in MS F 662
     only), and continuo (in all of the sources the continuo part is given
     for the solo sections only).

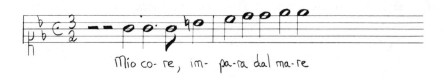

GB Och, 996, ff. 101-103, Luigi Rossi.
B Bc, F 662, pp. 113-118, Luigi Rossi.
I Rvat, Barb. lat. 4200, ff. 127-132v, anon.
D HVl, MS IV 422, pp. 29-30, anon. (the first soprano part only).

281.   Mortale, che pensi? Son caduchi i tuoi trionfi. Wo. 208, Gh. 363.
For two sopranos, alto, and continuo (the MSS 4200 and 996 have
the continuo part for the solo section only).

GB Och, 996, ff. 128-129v, Luigi Rossi.
B Bc, F 662, pp. 151-157, Luigi Rossi.
I Rvat, Barb. lat. 4200, ff. 92-95, anon.
I Bc, Q 50, ff. 35v-38, anon.
GB Lbm, Add. 31505, ff. 138-145v, anon.

282.   Noi siam tre donzellette semplicette, oh, senza fallo. Wo. 209, Gh.
365.
For three sopranos and continuo.

I Bc, Q 50, ff. 17-35v, Luigi.

283.   Piangea l'aurora, e del suo pianto rideano i fiori. Wo. 213, Gh. 370. For two sopranos, bass, and continuo.

GB Och, 996, ff. 87v-98. Luigi Rossi.
B Bc, F 662, pp. 69-99, Luigi Rossi.

284.   Quand'io credo esser disciolto in tranquilla libertà. Wo. 214, Gh. 372.
For soprano, alto, baritone (the lowest voice is notated on the bass staff in MS F 662 only), and continuo (F 662 has a continuo part; MSS 4200 and 996 lack it).

GB Och, 996, ff. 103v-105, Luigi Rossi.
B Bc, F 662, pp. 119-124, Luigi Rossi.
I Rvat, Barb. lat. 4200, ff. 124v-127, anon.

285.   Rugge quasi leon ch'habbi la febre; bestemia il ciel. Wo. 142, Gh. 211.
For three sopranos and continuo.

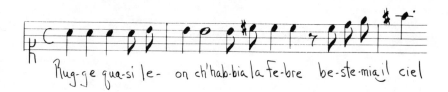

I Bc, Q 50, ff. 5v-14v, Luigi.

Wotquenne and Ghislanzoni erroneously list *Rugge quasi leon* as a solo cantata. The voices are marked "Testo," "Mustafà," and "Baiazet." The trio which occurs after the second solo and again at the end is marked "Choro."

At the beginning of the cantata the narrator tells of Amarat's order that his two brothers Mustafa and Baiazet be killed. The Amarat referred to is very likely Emperor Amurath IV of Turkey, who, in the summer of 1635, ordered his brothers Orchan and Bajazet killed.[19] It was by his order, too, that his uncle Mustafà, the previous Emperor, was strangled. If the name Mustafà be substituted for Orchan, it is evident that the fratricide lamented in the cantata is the royal fratricide of 1635.[20] Thus both the text and the music date from after August, 1635.

286. Sovra un lido che fremea d'atro pianto. Wo. 215, Gh. 273.
For two sopranos, bass, and continuo (the continuo part is lacking in the trio sections).

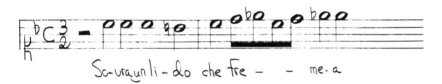

I Bc, Q 44, ff. 155v-162, Luigi Rossi.
US LAu, Special Collections 170/85, ff. 73-88v (f. 73 is torn away), anon.

287. Tu parti, core, addio. Va dove vuoi tu. Wo. 216, Gh. 374.
For soprano, alto, baritone or bass (the lowest voice is a baritone in MS 996; a bass in F 662), and continuo.

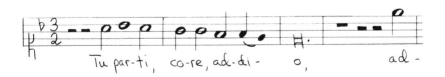

GB Och, 996, ff. 107v-108v, Luigi Rossi (lacks continuo).
B Bc, F 662, pp. 129-133 (not p. 44, as indicated in the previous cata-
logues), Luigi Rossi.
B Bc, F 663 (copy of F 662, with continuo realized by F. A. Gevaert).

Tu parti, core is not in GB Lbm, Add. 31505, given incorrectly by Ghislanzoni as a concordance.

288.   Udite, amanti, opra d'amor novella. Wo. 217, Gh. 375.
        For two sopranos, mezzo-soprano, and continuo.

GB Och, 996, ff. 79v-81, Luigi Rossi.
B Bc, F 662, pp. 44-50, Luigi Rossi.
GB Lbm, Add. 31505, ff. 173-176v, anon.
Eins, 86, 10-11 (copy of F 662).

(The lowest voice is not a soprano as indicated in the previous catalogues;
rather, in all sources, it is a mezzo-soprano.)

Quartets

289.   Cor dolente, ferito, schernito, non tacer se sei tradito. Wo. 218,
        Gh. 376.
        For soprano, alto, tenor, bass, and continuo.

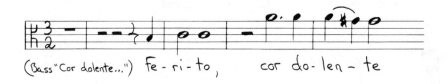

GB Och, 996, ff. 69v-71, Luigi Rossi (lacks text of 2d strophe).
B Bc, F 662, pp. 18-24, Luigi Rossi (lacks text of 2d strophe).

I Bc, Q 48, ff. 103-104v, anon. (lacks the quartet which is the third and final section in the two previous MSS, but has in its place the opening trio of which the quartet is a reworking.

Eins, 86, 4-5 (copy of F 662).

290.   Horche fra l'ombre del notturno velo. Wo. 219, Gh. 378.

For three sopranos, bass, and continuo (in the three sources the continuo part is omitted for the quartet, the final section).

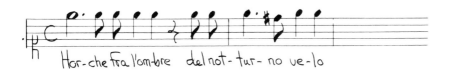

GB Och, 996, ff. 71v-73, Luigi Rossi.
B Bc, F 662, pp. 100-105, Luigi Rossi.
I Rvat, Barb. lat. 4200, ff. 151-155, anon.

291.   Pur è ver che fiero danno è compagno del piacere. Wo. 220, Gh. 379.

For three sopranos, bass, and continuo (the sources lack the continuo for all the quartet sections).

GB Och, 996, ff. 63v-69, Luigi Rossi.
B Bc, F 662, pp. 2-17, Luigi Rossi.
Eins, 86, 1-4 (copy of F 662).

292. Su, su, begl'occhi, su, su, date pace al mio core.
      For two sopranos, alto, bass and continuo.

US LAu, Special Collections 170/85, ff. 185-200, Luigi Rossi.

Notes for Thematic Index 1

1. Lady Sidney Morgan, *The Life and Times of Salvator Rosa* (London, 1824), I, 314. note.

2. Uberto Limentani, *Poesie e Lettere inedite di Salvator Rosa* (Firenze, Olschki, 1950), p. 14, note 26. Ghislanzoni, op. cit., p. 167.

3. Alberto Cametti "Alcuni documenti inediti su la vita di Luigi Rossi . . .," *SIMG*, XIV (1912), p. 19.

4. Pietro Della Valle, "Della musica dell'eta nostra," January 16, 1640, in Giovanni Battista Doni, *De' Trattati di Musica* (Florence, 1763), II, 249-264; reprinted in Angelo Solerti, *Le Origini del Melodramma* . . . (Torino, 1903), pp. 148-179 (the passage of concern here is on p. 168).

5. As an example of the lively kind of new music, Della Valle cites Horatio's *Per torbido mare*. In the MS Barb. lat. 4151 (I Rvat) there is an anonymous setting of *Per torbido mare* which is most likely the one by Horatio since the contents of the MS date from the period to which Della Valle refers. Furthermore, Barb. lat. 4151, whose contents are anonymous, is related to the MSS I Rc, 2490 and Rbn, 56, in which there are pieces attributed to Horatio (Orazio dell Arpa) or attributable to him by concordances. It is reasonable to presume that the composers represented in the MSS related to 4151 also composed some of the pieces in 4151.

6. Charles Burney, *A General History of Music* (London, 1776-1789), Dover edition of 1957, II, 524-534, quotes from and discusses the letter; the passage of concern here is quoted and paraphrased on p. 532. (The quotations are translated in English.) Also: Francois Joseph Fetis, *Biographie universelle* . . . (Paris, 1860-1865), VII, 316. Henry Prunieres, *L'Opera Italien en France* . . . (Paris, 1913), p. 23. Alberto Ghislanzoni, *Luigi Rossi*, op. cit., p. 55.

7. Limentani, *Poesie* . . ., op. cit., p. 14, note 26, errs in locating *Horche la notte* in GB Lbm, Harl. 1265.

8. The MS 56 in which *Horche la notte* appears has concordances for pieces in the MSS I Rc, 2490; Rvat, Barb. lat. 4151; Bc, Q 49 (see below, no. 98) and Q 43, whose contents are related stylistically and date from the second and third decades of the century, the period of the new music named by Della Valle.

9. Lady Sidney Morgan, loc. cit., says that the words "are supposed to have been written by Salvator Rosa." There is no evidence, however, to support this hypothesis.

10. Ghislanzoni, op. cit., pp. 112-115.

11. The four pieces by Luigi in Harl. 1273 are also in 4718a; three are in the same consecutive order. Harl. 1273 is the later manuscript, for composers as late as Alessandro Scarlatti and Bononcini are represented in it. The composers represented in 4718a are no later than Carissimi, Cavalli, Savioni, Caprioli, and Cesti. Harl. 1273 agrees in detail with 4718a in the copies of Luigi's pieces; it is reasonable to presume, therefore, that the former is a copy of the latter.

12. Francesco Cognasso, *Storia di Torino* (Turin, 1934), pp. 133-135.

13. It is Carlo Emanuel I that Gianbattista Marino addresses in *Il Pianto D'Italia* towards the end:

> Già dell'Italia i liberati regni
> Inalzano al tuo nome e bronzi e marmi;
> E mille rari e fortunati ingegni
> Scrivono le tue vittorie e cantan l'armi.

(See *Opere* [Napoli, 1861], pp. 551 ff.) Carlo is associated in several poems with Italy's hopes for liberation from foreign oppression; see Benedetto Croce, *Storia Dell'Età Barocca in Italia* (Bari, 1957), pp. 413-415.

14. Ghislanzoni, pp. 209-211, publishes the text in its entirety.

15. Wotquenne, in the Preface to his *Etude*, is the first to mention Tenaglia's reference to Luigi's cantata.

16. Henry Prunières, *L'Opera Italien en France avant Lulli* (Paris, 1913), p. 46.

17. See *WECIS*, Fasc. 4.

18. It may be such an insertion that Alberto Limentani, *Enciclopedia dello Spettacolo* (Rome, 1960), Vol. VII, col. 313, refers to as the "elementi estranei" in Minato's *L'Artemisia*.

19. Richard Knolles, *The Turkish History From the Original of that Nation to the Growth of the Growth of the Ottoman Empire* . . . (London, 1687), II, 31 and 48.

20. This fratricide was known and discussed in Italy, for Bajazet's imprisonment and murder also inspired Salvator Rosa's canzone *Che non deve l'uomo fidarsi nella pospera fortuna*.

In this poem Bajazet laments his fate and gives warning to those in possession of power and wealth not to depend on fortune. Limentani, op. cit., pp. 163-165, prints the last 5 strophes and gives variant readings for some of the verses in the complete version published by Ozzola, *Vita e opera di Salvator Rosa* . . . (Strassburg, 1908), pp. 222 ff.

Thematic Index 2

Cantatas Attributed to Luigi Rossi
on Unreliable Grounds

293.   Affetto più bizzarro di questo ch'io vi narro al mondo mai s'udì.
Gh. 6.

I Rvat, Barb. lat. 4208, ff. 130v-135v, anon.

294.   Aita, aita, o cieli, aita! Già dal soglio di Persia. Gh. 7.

I Rvat, Barb. lat. 4200, ff. 1-10, anon.

295.   Alle note affannose che mandò Zaida al suo fedel. Gh. 10.

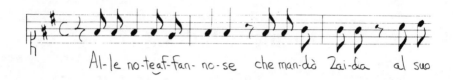

I Rvat, Barb. lat. 4200, ff. 10v-18v, anon. (has the title "Mustafà").

Although no author's name is mentioned in this MS, Ghislanzoni, relating this cantata to *Sparsa il crine*, no. 184 above, attributes the text to Fabio della Corgnia. *Sparsa il crine* is the lament of the Turk Zaida for her lover Mustafà, captured by the Tuscan navy. Mustafà, in *Alle note affannose* replies to Zaida from Tuscany where, by the kindness of Ferdinand, he lives a free man. The event referred to in both texts is, without doubt, the victory of the Tuscan navy over the Turkish fleet in 1608 during the reign of Ferdinand I, when seven hundred prisoners were taken.[1]

296.   Amor arozza i cori con l'insegna d'un bel guardo. Gh. 16.

I Rvat, Barb. lat. 4204, f. 10, anon.

297.   Amor con strana doglia tiranneggia suberbo. Gh. 17.

I Rvat, Barb. lat. 4208, ff. 118-121, anon.

298.   Amor, sai perchè così tu m'oltraggi. Gh. 21.

I Rvat, Barb. lat. 4208, ff. 34-37, anon.
I Rc, 2466, ff. 217-223, anon.
I PAc, CF-111-1, ff. 144-150, anon.

299.   Ancor vive una speranza che dell'alma resto sciolta. Wo. 17, Gh.
        23.

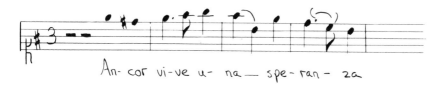

GB Och, 947, ff. 109-111v, luigi (the attribution is not in the hand of the
text).

300.   Apen' hebbe Filandro lette e rilette.

I Rc, 2505, ff. 62-76v, anon.
A Wn, 18610, ff. 10-17, anon. (has the title "Pedante innamorato").
B Bc, F 12.900, pp. 13-22 (copy of 18610).

Wotquenne lists *Apen' hebbe Filandro* under "Oeuvres douteuses ou
apocryphes."

301.   A più sventure ancora serberò questa vita.

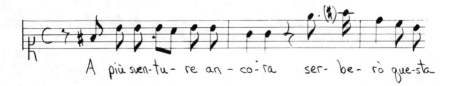

GB Och, 947, ff. 51-60v, luigi (the attribution is not in the hand of the text).
F Pthibault, Rec.H.P.6, pp. 69-89, Atto Melani.

302.   Ardo per te, ben mio, ma vuole il crudo amore. Gh. 27.

I Rvat, Barb. lat. 4200, ff. 56-57, anon.

303.   Augellin di sete acceso, io ti lascio. Gh. 32.

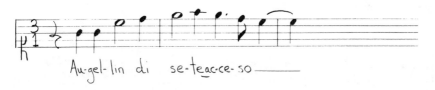

I Rvat, Barb. lat. 4200, ff. 37-38, anon.
I Rvat, Chigi Q IV 8, ff. 36-37v, anon.
Another setting, for two sopranos and continuo (see above, no. 211):
I Fc, D 2357, ff. 33v-38, Luigi.

304. Begl'occhi, pietà! son vinto. Gh. 36.

I Rvat, Barb. lat. 4200, ff. 63-65, anon.
Another setting, for soprano solo (see above, no. 25):
F Pn, Vm7 6, f. 13, Luigi Rossi.

305. Begl'occhi tiranni, e dove s'intese. Gh. 37.

I Rvat, Barb. lat. 4208, ff. 89-91v, anon.

306. Bella cosa sarebbe amore se non fosse la crudeltà. Gh. 38.

I Rvat, Barb. lat. 4208, ff. 126-130, anon.

Ghislanzoni's incipit incorrectly has "ancora" in place of the word "amore."

307.   Cara bocca se ride o parla o se scocca dai labri. Gh. 40.

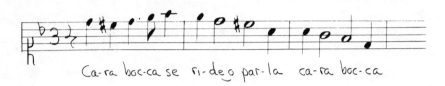

I Rvat, Barb. lat. 4208, ff. 140v-144, anon.
GB Lbm, Harl. 1266, ff. 83-92v, anon.
B Bc, F. A. VI. 23, ff. 9-16v, anon.

308.   C è altra pena che morire, s'io, begl'occhi, v'amerò.

GB Och, 948, ff. 11-19, Luigi (the attribution is not in the hand of the
    text).
I Nc, 60.1.51, no. 14, anon.
Another version, for soprano solo:
B Bc, F. A. VI 22, ff. 11-18v, Giovanni Bicilli.
I MOe, Mus. E. 300, ff. 25-28, anon.
Yet another version, for soprano solo:
I Rvat, Chigi Q IV 2, ff. 91-96, Giovanni Battista Gianscosi.

309.   Ch'amor sia foco, io mene rido. Gh. 42.

I Rvat, Barb. lat. 4175, ff. 37-39, anon. (incomplete).

I Rvat, Barb. lat. 4221, ff. 137-138v, anon.

Il mio cor, signora, sclama, I Rvat, Barb. lat. 4221, ff. 87-89, anon., has the same ostinato bass, is composed in the same tonality, has the same meter, and the bass notes have the same metrical values.

310.   Che ti resta, o mio core? Ingrata è la beltà. Gh. 47.

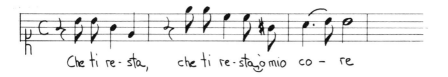

I Rvat, Barb. lat. 4208, ff. 111v-114v, anon.
F Pn, Vm7 1, ff. 102-113v, anon.
B Bc, F. A. VI. 20, ff. 29-40v, anon.
I MAC, MS Mus. 78, ff. 152-155v, anon.

311.   Che volete da me, vani pensieri? Wo. 32, Gh. 48, Re. 3.

GB Cfm, 24.F.4, ff. 106v-108v, Luigi Rossi.
GB Lbm, Harl. 1264, ff. 51v-58, anon.
I Rvat, Chigi Q IV 18, ff. 81-88v, Alessandro Melani.
A Wn, 17758, ff. 49-58v, Alesandro (sic) Melani.
B Bc, 17193, pp. 195-199 (copy of 24.F.4).

Both Wotquenne and Ghislanzoni give I Rvat, Barb. lat. 4163, ff. 32v ff. as a concordance, but only the first four words of the text are the same; the music is altogether different.

312.   Chiuda quest'occhi il sonno s'immagini si belle. Gh. 59.

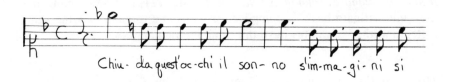

I Rc, 2467, ff. 53v-59, Luigi Rossi.
I Rvat, Barb. lat. 4220, ff. 59-60v, anon.
I Rvat, Barb. lat. 4374, pp. 147-152, anon. (for tenor).
I Rvat, Barb. lat. 4175, ff. 81v-85, MAP.

313.   Con incerta speranza di poter impetrar tegua a le pene. Wo. 45,
       Gh. 64.

GB Och, 949, ff. 85-90v, Luigi.
I Rvat, Chigi Q VIII 180, ff. 69-70, anon. (Marco Marazzoli).
I Nc, 33.4.18, II, 65-73, Carissimi.
I Rc, 2468, ff. 91-96v, Marco Marazzoli.

314.   Con rauco mormorio sciogliea lubrico il piede. Wo. 47, Gh. 66.

I Rvat, Chigi Q IV 8, ff. 37v-45v, Luigi Rossi (the attribution is not in the
hand of the text).

GB Och, 951, ff. 1-11v, Luigi Rossi (the attribution is not in the hand of
the text).

I G1, A-5-Cass., ff. 187-202v, Antimo Liberati.

The attribution Luigi Rossi at the head of the strophe "Ruscelletto che
te'n vai," f. 39v of Q IV 8, may have misled Cametti, who lists it separately.[2] Ghislanzoni does likewise (catalogue no. 212). "Ruscelleto" is
the second of the nine sections that form the cantata.

315.   Credei col gir lontano dal bel'idolo mio. Wo. 49, Gh. 69.

GB Och, 946, ff. 15-24v, luigi (the attribution is not in the hand of the
text).

GB Lbm, Harl. 1266, ff. 126-135v, anon.

B Bc, 15258, pp. 11-15, Luigi Rossi (copy of Harl. 1266).

316.   Dà gli abissi dell'Herebo sù, furie, scatenatevi. Gh. 70.

I Rvat, Barb. lat. 4204, ff. 44-54v, anon.

I Rvat, Barb. lat. 4205, ff. 177-184v, anon.

I Rvat, Barb. lat. 4223, ff. 137-144v, MAP.

317.   Dagli occhi un mar puoi tu ben piove. Gh. 71.

I Rvat, Barb. lat. 4175, ff. 101-102, anon.

318.   Del silenzio il giogo algente spezzi, homai, la lingua. Wo. 53, Gh.
         75.

GB Och, 952, ff. 1-10v, Luigi (the attribution is not in the hand of the
    text).
D, pp. 195-199 (copy of 952).

319.   Dentro negra foresta dove già la portò. Gh. 76.

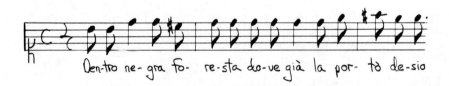

I Rvat, Barb. lat. 4208, ff. 37v-43, anon.

320. Disperati, cor mio, e che sperar. Gh. 80.

I Rvat, Barb. lat. 4175, ff. 33v-35, anon. (the continuo part is incomplete).
I Rvat, Barb. lat. 4220, ff. 31-32, anon., text by Giovanni Lotti.

321. Dove miri, pensiero? Ferma, troppo alto. Gh. 184.

I Rvat, Barb. lat. 4175, ff. 39v-45, anon.

322. E che ti costa un guardo, empia che sei. Gh. 68.

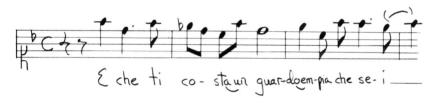

I Rvat, Barb. lat. 4200, ff. 40-41, anon.

323. E chi non piangerebbe al pianto mio. Gh. 87.

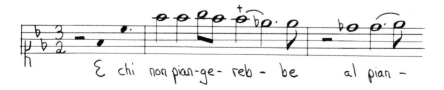

I Rvat, Barb. lat. 4204, ff. 21-28v, anon.

324.   E pur mi lusingate, amorosi pensieri. Gh. 90.

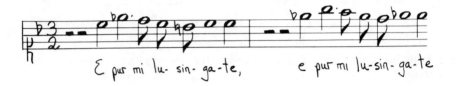

I Rvat, Barb. lat. 4175, ff. 79v-81, anon.
B Br, II 3947, ff. 59-62v, anon.
Eins, 87, 13 (copy of II 3947).

325.   Fammi giustitia, amore, odi le mie querele.

Gb Och, 946, ff. 33-38, anon.
I Nc, 33.5.27, ff. 47-50v, Domenico Antº DeMundo.

Wotquenne, unaware of the concordance in 33.5.27 with the attribution
DeMundo, lists this cantata under "Oeuvres douteuses ou apocryphes."

326.   Farfalletta che ten vai invaghita al foco ardente. Gh. 95.

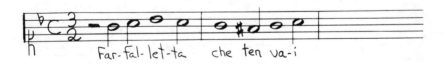

I Nc, 33.4.15, I, 31-35v, Luiggi Rossi.

I Rvat, Chigi Q VIII 177, ff. 168v-170, anon. (Marco Marazzoli).

327. Ferma, Daphne, ah, pertinace, perche fuggi un nume amante?

F Pn, Vm7 6, ff. 22-23, anon.

Ecorcheville, op. cit. VII, 188, mistakenly lists this composition with those attributed to Luigi Rossi.

328. Ferma il piè, taci ed ascolta. Wo. 68, Gh. 97.

GB Och, 946, ff. 1-12v, luigi (the attribution is not in the hand of the text).
F Pthibault, Rec. H. P. 7, ff. 29-48v, anon.
I Nc, 33.4.15, II, 73-88v, Carlo del Violino.

329. Filli mia, altro ci vuole. Wo. 69, Gh. 98.

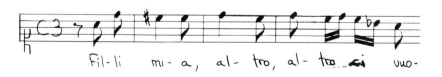

GB Och, 947, ff. 105-108v, luigi (the attribution is not in the hand of the text).

330.   Fra le pene dello stral che mi ferì. Wo. 70, Gh. 99.

GB Och, 947, ff. 87-92v, luigi (the attribution is not in the hand of the text).

331.   Furie d'averno uditemi, impiagate. Wo. 71, Gh. 100.

Incipit A: (Vm7 11a & 51)

Incipit B: (946)

GB Och, 946, ff. 81-88v, luigi (the attribution is not in the hand of the text).
F Pn, Vm7 11a, pp. 5-21, anon.
I Rdp, 51, pp. 97-104, D'incerto.
B Bc, 15261, pp. 9-14 (copy of 946).

332. Già dalla bella aurora arrichiti. Gh. 102.

I Rvat, Barb. lat. 4208, ff. 22-28v, anon.
I Rc, 2466, ff. 1-12v, anon.

333. Già fiero il tormento s'accrescan le pene. Gh. 103.

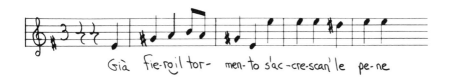

I Rvat, Barb. lat. 4208, ff. 21-22, anon.

334. Già lo so che tocca à me di penar. Gh. 105.

I Rvat, Barb. lat. 4208, ff. 70-72, anon.
I Rvat, Barb. lat. 4205, ff. 163v-164, anon.
Another setting for soprano solo:
F Pa, M. 948, ff. 72v-74v, anon.

335.   Gioir non si può quando il sospetto. Gh. 107.

I Rvat, Barb. lat. 4208, ff. 14-16, anon.
I Rc, 2477, ff. 147-152v, anon.
I Rvat, Chigi Q VIII 180, ff. 61v-62v, anon. (Marco Marazzoli).

336.   Gionto il fatale dì che Clorindo vezzose. Wo. 75, Gh. 108.

GB Och, 950, ff. 11-20, Luigi (the attribution is not in the hand of the
text).
I Nc, 33.4.12, II, 1-22, Provenzale (for mezzo-soprano, transposed to g
minor).

337.   Havessi, ohimè, quando la lingua sciolsi. Wo. 24, Gh. 33.

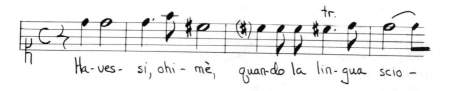

F Pn, Rés, Vm7 59, ff. 91-94v, anon.
B Bc, 15258, pp. 5-7, Luigi Rossi (copy of Rés. Vm7 59).

In the alphabetical index of the MS Rés. Vm7 59, where the attributions
follow the text incipits, *Havessi, ohimè!* is anonymous. The copyist of

the MS 15258 errs in attributing the piece to Rossi. Wotquenne, misled by this copy, includes the cantata in his catalogue, and Ghislanzoni retains it in his. Gevaert, who in his notebook (B Bc, XY 8286, pp. 65-71) lists all of the pieces in Rés. Vm7 59 attributed to Luigi Rossi, does not include *Havessi, ohimè!* among them.

338.   Hor va, mio core, serba intatta. Gh. 183.

I Rvat, Barb. lat. 4221, ff. 85-86, anon.
I Rvat, Barb. lat. 4204, ff. 138-139, anon. (incomplete).

339.   Il celeste arator se mira apena. Gh. 41.

I Rvat, Barb. lat. 4175, ff. 85v-91, anon.
I Rvat, Barb. lat. 4223, ff. 39-42, MAP, text by Lelio Guidiccioni.

340.   Il mio core, chi l'ha? dov'è? Wo. 79, Gh. 114, Re. 83.

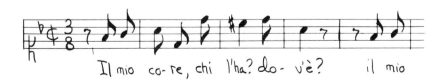

GB Och, 951, ff. 68-70v, Luigi Rossi (the attribution is not in the hand of the text).
GB Lbm, Harl. 1266, ff. 142-148v, anon.
F Pthibault, Rec. H.P. 31, pp. 47-49, anon. (lacks text of 2d strophe; the 1st strophe begins "Il mio cuore chi sa dov'è").
A Wn, 17765, ff. 59-64v, anon.
B Bc, 17197, pp. 138-142 (copy of Harl. 1266).

341. Il mondo della bellezza ha sempre nel sen la congiura. Gh. 115.

I Rvat, Barb. lat. 4200, ff. 47v-48v, anon.
F Pn, Vm7 10, ff. 10v-12, anon. (arranged for soprano, bass, and continuo).

342. Indovinala, mio core, altrimente io mi dispero. Wo. 80, Gh. 116.

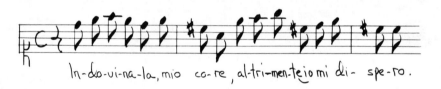

GB Och, 949, ff. 91-94, luigi (the attribution is not in the hand of the text).
Another setting, for bass solo:
I MOe, Mus. G. 307, ff. 15-18, anon.

343. In questa oscuritade horrida e negra. Gh. 119.

I Rvat, Barb. lat. 4208, ff. 121-125v, anon.
GB CKc, MS 22, ff. 189v-192, Carlo del Violino.

344.   In si dura lontananza dove volgo il piede. Gh. 120.

I Rvat, Barb. lat. 4208, ff. 54v-57v, anon.

345.   Languia Filen trafitto, doleasi incatenato. Wo. 88, Gh. 128.

GB Och, 950, ff. 69-78, luigi (the attribution is not in the hand of the text).
I Nc, 33.5.33, ff. 65-70v, anon.
I Nc, 33.4.17, II, 157-170v, anon. (the attribution Carissimi is a later
    addition).
I Rvat, Chigi Q IV 11, ff. 16-31v, Carlo Caprioli.

346.   La speranza ch'è cibo del core. Gh. 133.

I Nc, 33.5.33, ff. 7v-8v, Luigi Rossi (the attribution is not in the hand of
    the text).

347.   Lusinghiero desio ch'il moribondo cor nutrì di spene. Gh. 137.

I Rvat, Barb. lat. 4175, ff. 98v-100v, anon.

348.   Mene contento, non ricuso pena alcuna. Gh. 139.

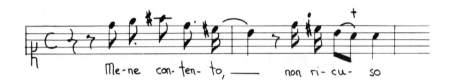

I Rvat, Barb. lat. 4208, ff. 72v-75v, anon.
I Rc, 2475, ff. 53-58v, anon.
GB Och, 953, ff. 35v-41, anon.
I Rc, 2468, ff. 73-80v, Carlo dal Violino.

349.   Mentre la notte havea d'horror indegno. Gh. 140.

I Rvat, Barb. lat. 4200, ff. 52v-55v, anon. (has the heading "Sonetto").

350.   Mezza tra viva e morta su duro sasso. Gh. 142.

I Rvat, Barb. lat. 4175, ff. 1-23v, anon. (has the title "Olimpia").
I Rc, 2505, ff. 125v-134v, anon.

351.   Mi dispiace dirl'hoime, ma bisogno ch'io lo dica. Gh. 144.

I Nc, 33.4.15, I, 129-139v, Luigi Rossi (the attribution is not in the hand
of the text).

352.   Mi vogliono morto due lumi guerrieri. Gh. 147.

I Rvat, Barb. lat. 4204, ff. 141-142v, anon.
I Rvat, Barb. lat. 4220, ff. 51v-52v, anon.
I Rvat, Barb. lat. 4203, ff. 125v-127, MAP.

Ghislanzoni errs in identifying this melody with that of *Si tocchi tamburo*,
the final solo aria in Luigi's opera *Il Palazzo Incantato*. Only the first two
measures are the same.

353.   Non ci voglio pensar più se non fai quel che voglio.

B Br, II 3947, ff. 125-128v, anon. (lacks text of 2d strophe).
B Bc, XY 8286, pp. 87-88 (copy of II 3947 by Gevaert, who remarks
    "Cantata di autore anonimo (Luigi Rossi?).")
Another setting for soprano solo:
I Rvat, Chigi Q IV 5, ff. 25-26, anon.

354.   Non fia mai, benchè impiagata che quest'alma. Wo. 104, Gh. 155.

GB Och, 952 (not 947, as Wotquenne and Ghislanzoni indicate), ff. 39-46v,
    luigi (the attribution is not in the hand of the text).

355.   Non m'asciugate il pianto ch'à torrenti il volto inonda. Wo. 106,
    Gh. 158, Re. 20.

D K1, 2° Mus.34, ff. 49v-50v, Luigi Rossi (lacks text of 2d strophe).
I Nc, 33.4.19, II, 161-164v, anon. (in a minor).
F Pn, Vm7 1, ff. 29-34v, anon.
I MOe, Mus.G 106, Alessandro Leardini.
B Bc, 17197, pp. 95-98 (copy of 2° Mus. 34).

356.   Non mi negar ch'io speri, cieco che miri tutti i desiri. Gh. 160.

I Rvat, Barb. lat. 4175, ff. 63v-65, anon.

357.   Non mi turbate più, pensieri amanti. Gh. 161.

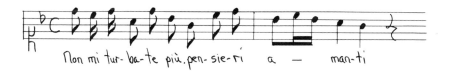

I Rvat, Barb. lat. 4208, ff. 84-88v, anon.
F Pn, Vm7 8, ff. 73v-75, anon. (lacks continuo).

358.   Nò, nò, fuggir non vò; seguirò fin che spiro. Gh. 162, Re. 69.

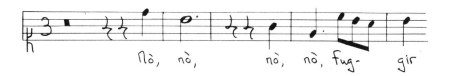

D SW, 4718a, pp. 79-82, anon. (lacks text of 2d strophe).
GB Lbm, Harl. 1273, ff. 77-77v, anon. (lacks text of 2d strophe). The aria
   is erroneously attached to *Nè notte nè di*; see above, no. 122.
B Bc, 17193, pp. 192-194 (copy of Harl. 1273). Wotquenne also follows
   Nè notte nè di with this aria as if the two belonged together.

In a libretto of Cicognini's *Orontea* at the Biblioteca Nazionale in Florence (the Venice edition of 1666) the aria *Nò, nò, fuggir non vò* (with the
text of a second strophe) is assigned to Corindo in scene 11, Act III. But
the text does not appear in the other libretto at the same library (the
Florence edition of 1661), nor in the two libretti at the Library of Congress, one without date, the other dated 1662. Moreover it is not present
in the extant musical score of the opera.[3] It may be that the musical
setting listed here is the one inserted in the particular performance of
Orontea represented by the 1666 libretto, for no other setting of this text
is extant. Who the composer of this aria is, however, remains unknown.

359. Non si parli di ventura troppo dura a tutte l'hore. Wo. 110. Gh. 165.

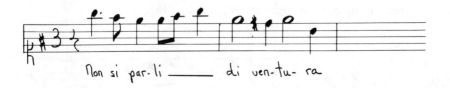

GB Och, 951, ff. 13-20v, luigi (the attribution is not in the hand of the text).

I Nc, 33.4.16, ff. 39-45, anon.

GB Cfm, 24 F 21, anon.

F Pc, D 11837, ff. 137v-143, anon. The attribution "Libro De Cantate Del Signore Alessandro Scarlatti" on the title folio cannot be identified with the hand of either copyist. It is probably unreliable.

360.   Non superbite, amanti, i rivi del goder. Gh. 166.

I Rvat, Barb. lat. 4200, ff. 19-25, anon.

361.   Non ti doler, cor mio, se la cruda beltà non palesa. Gh. 167.

I Rvat, Barb. lat. 4175, ff. 94v-96v, anon.

Another setting for soprano solo:

US CA, MS Mus 106, no. 42, ff. (127-128v), anon.

362.   Oblio che lento e tacito mi vai serpendo il core. Gh. 168.

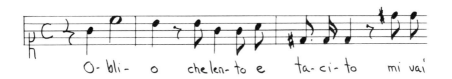

I Rvat, Chigi Q VII 99, ff. 17-22, anon.
I Nc, 33.3.11, ff. 26-30, anon.

363.   Occhi miei belli, occhi adorati, occhi beati, che furon quelli.

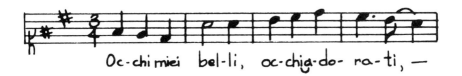

US LA, MS fC 697, M.4, pp. 38-45, Luigi Rossi.
I Fn, Magl. XIX.26, f. 15, Atto Melani.
D Mbs, 1524, ff. 119-123, anon.
F Pthibault, Rec. H.P.6, pp. 1-2, anon.
F Pn, Vm7 18, pp. 65-67, anon. (strophes 1 and 3; strophe 2 is omitted).
B Bc, 17196, pp. 181-184 (possibly a copy of MS 1524).

364.   Ò, ch'humore stravagante ch'è colei che servo. Wo. 114, Gh. 174.

GB Och, 951, ff. 29-32, luigi (the attribution does not seem to be in the
    hand of the text).
I Fbn, Magl. XIX 26, ff. 69v-75, Antonio Sartorio.

Pa, III, 48-56, Antonio Sartorio. The editor does not give his source, but only indicates that the piece is a "fragment of a comic Intermedium."

365.   O cor che mi lasciasti pero ch'incauto. Gh. 171.

I Rvat, Barb. lat. 4175, ff. 97-98, anon.

366.   O quante punture mi sento nel core.

F Pthibault, Rec. H.P.5, ff. 37-43, luigi (the ascription is very faint and to the left of the illuminated initial letter).
B Bc, F.A.VI 20, ff. 171-180v, Antonio Francesco Tenaglia.
I Busseto, Villa Verdi, an unclassified MS dated 1689; the cantata, the second in the MS, is attributed to Tenaglia.

367.   Ove tenebre, ohimè, ove fuggite? Gh. 185.

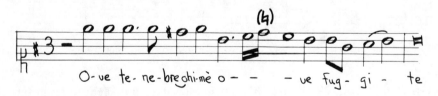

I Rvat, Barb. lat. 4200, ff. 43-45v, anon.

368. Passati contenti, e dove n'andaste. Wo. 125, Gh. 188.

GB Och, 946, ff. 73-80, luigi (the attribution is not in the hand of the text).
F Pn, Vm7 4, pp. 335-361, anon.
B Bc, 15258, pp. 3-4, incomplete (copy of Vm7 4).
Another setting for soprano solo:
F Pthibault, Rec. H.P.1, ff. 163-174, Anton Maria Abbatini.

369. Per placare la diva ch'adoro.

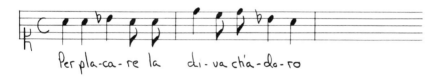

F Pn, Vm7 6, f. 26v, anon.

Erroneously attributed to Luigi Rossi in Ecorcheville, VII, 189.

370. Per un guardo del mio bene che darei? Gh. 194.

I Rvat, Barb. lat. 4204, ff. 75-76v, anon.
I Rvat, Barb. lat. 4220, ff. 29-30, anon., text by Lotti.
I Rvat, Barb. lat. 4219, ff. 211-213v, anon., text by Gio. Lotti. (arranged
    for soprano, bass, and continuo).

I Nc, 33.4.19, II, ff. 145-150v, MAP.

371.   Poiche il lido sicano lasciato Eurillo havea. Wo. 130, Gh. 195.

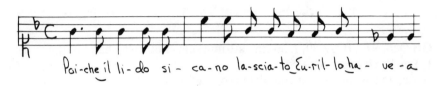

Poi-che il li-do si - ca-no la-scia-to Eu-ril-lo ha - ve -a

GB Och, 946, ff. 65-72v, luigi (the attribution is not in the hand of the text).

372.   Porto d'ascose fiamme il cor. Wo. 131, Gh. 196.

Por- to d'a-sco-se fiam-me   il _____   cor lan -

GB Och, 951, ff. 33-38v, luigi (the attribution is not in the hand of the text).

373.   Pupillette mie belle, occhi cari ch'adoro. Gh. 200.

Pu-pil-let-te mie bel-le,   pu-pil-let-te mie bel-le

I Rvat, Barb. lat. 4175, ff. 31v-33, anon.
Another setting for soprano solo:
D Mbs, 1524, ff. 52-55v, anon.
B Bc, 17196, pp. 175-179 (copy of 1524).

—Ruscelletto che te'n vai. Gh. 212.

See Con rauco mormorio sciogliea, no. 314 above.

374.   Sassi, ch'or qui tra le ruine el herbe godete.

F Pn, Vm7 6, ff. 24-25, Luigi Rossi.
I MOe, Mus. G. 42, Carissimi (the first words are "Sassi, e hor quà").
B Bc, 17186 (copy of Mus. G. 42).
B Bc, 15261, p. 48 (incomplete). Wotquenne began copying from Vm7 6,
   but discontinued when he recalled that the Brussels Conservatory li-
   brary possessed a copy of Mus. G. 42. Wotquenne lists *Sassi, ch'or qui*
   under "Oeuvres douteuses ou apocryphes."
Another setting, for bass solo:
GB Lbm, Harl. 1501, ff. 61-63v, Pietro Reggio, text by Cavaglier Marini.[4]
GB Lbm, Harl. 1863, ff. 43v-46v, Pietro Reggio.
B Bc, F. 660 (copy of Harl. 1501).

375.   Se barbari legami prepara all'alma. Wo. 143, Gh. 213.

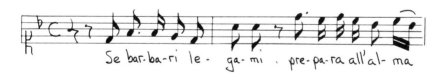

GB Och, 951, ff. 39-42v, luigi (the attribution is not in the hand of the
   text).
I Nc, 33.4.17, I, 169-172v, anon. (the attribution Caprioli is a later addition).

376.   Se l'antica mia guerriera col suo stral. Gh. 215.

I Rvat, Barb. lat. 4200, ff. 41v-43, anon.
Another version for soprano solo:
I Nc, 33.4.17, ff. 95-103, Carissimi.

377.   Sempre in fasce, ò mio desire. Gh. 217.

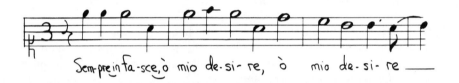

I Rvat, Barb. lat. 4200, ff. 35v-36v, anon.

378.   Se noto ti fò quel stravagante affetto. Gh. 220.

I Rvat, Barb. lat. 4208, ff. 135v-140v, anon.

379.   Sensi, voi ciò che godete.

I Rc, 2468, ff. 201-205v, Luigi.

I Rvat, Barb. lat. 4207, ff. 75-80, anon.

F Pthibault, Rec. H.P. 4, ff. 36-41, anon.

F Pthibault, Libro di Salvator Rosa, no. 16, ff. 46-46v, anon., and incomplete.

GB Lbm, Harl. 1501, ff. 23v-25v, Padre Cesti.

B Bc, 588, no. 2 (copy of Harl. 1501).

The aria "Pensieri contentatevi," measures 28-50, is either quoted from or quoted in Cesti's opera *Alessandro vincitor di se stesso*, for the same music tranposed a tone lower is used there for the aria "Se ben cruda e inesorabile." David Burrows, "The Cantatas of Antonio Cesti," unpublished dissertation (Brandeis University, 1961), pp. 72-73, gives the music of both arias.

The text is published by Limentani, pp. 52-53, who also gives evidence that the author is Salvator Rosa (pp. 17-18).

380.   Se peni tuo danno, ò pazzo mio core. Wo. 146, Gh. 221, Re. 11.

GB Och, 952 (not 947 as indicated in the previous catalogues), ff. 29-38, luigi (the attribution is not in the hand of the text).

I MOe, Mus. F. 1349, no. 11, anon.

B Bc, 17197, pp. 1-7 (copy by Wotquenne).

Rk, I, 60-68, Luigi Rossi. (Photographs of these pages are in Robert B. Morris, "A Study of the Italian Solo Cantata Before 1750," unpublished dissertation (Indiana University, 1955), pp. 31-36.

381.   Sì, ch'io v'amo, begl'occhi. Gh. 223.

I Rvat, Barb. lat. 4175, ff. 29v-31, anon.
Another setting for soprano solo:
D Mbs, 1524, ff. 159-161v, anon.
Yet another setting for soprano solo:
F Pn, Rés. Vm7 59, ff. 127-128v, Mario Savioni, text by Domenico Benigni.

382.   So ben io dov'è legata. Wo. 149, Gh. 225.

GB Och, 946, ff. 39-45v, luigi (the attribution is not in the hand of the text).
I Nc, 33.4.14, I, 106v-111, anon. (the attribution Carissimi is a later addition).

383.   Soccorretemi ch'io moro, occhi belli, oh Dio, pietà.

GB Och, 947, ff. 81-86v, luigi (the attribution is not in the hand of the text).
I Bc, X 234, ff. 25-30v, anon.
I Rvat, Barb. lat. 4136, ff. 171-177v, anon.
B Bc, F.A.VI 23, ff. 33-44v, anon.
I MOe, Mus.G.257, ff. 16-20v, Carissimi (in c minor).
I Vc, Busta 16-48-N. 47, Carissimi.
I Nc, 33.4.7, I, 59v-64v, Carissimi.
La, pp. 40-48.

384.   Sola fra suoi più cari à piè del Figlio afflitto.

I Fbn, Magl. XIX.22. The MS has been missing since 1883; the table of contents (in Vol. VI of the handwritten catalogues, p. 61) lists this piece as the "Cantata del Cav. Marino sopra lo *Stabat Mater*, messa in musica dal medesimo Rossi" (Aloigi de Rossi napolitano in Roma is the attribution given for the preceding composition). See also Bianca Becherini, *Catalogo dei MSS, Musicali della Biblioteca Nazionale di Firenze* (Kassel, 1959), p. 6.

A musical setting of Marino's *Stabat Mater* is extant in the MSS listed below; it may be the same work as that attributed to Luigi in the lost MS, or it may be a second setting of the text.

I Bc, Q 43, ff. 92-96, anon. (has the title "Pianto di Maria Vergine alla Croce").

I Rbn, 56, ff. 37-42, anon.

I Rc, 2490, pp. 124-129, Orazio dell'Arpa (has the title "Lamento della S(antissi)ma Vergine").

The text is published in Giovanni Battista Marino, *La Lira, Rime* (Venetia: Ciotti 1629), II, 143-147. Only thirteen of the twenty-five strophes are set to music.

385.   Sommergetemi, o pianti, sospir rapite. Gh. 226.

I Rvat, Barb. lat. 4208, ff. 96-101, anon.

386.   Sovra un sasso addolorata stette un dì. Gh. 232.

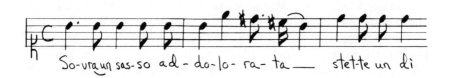

I Rvat, Barb. lat. 4208, ff. 1-4, anon.

387.   Sprigionami, ò sdegno, da regno d'amore. Gh. 235.

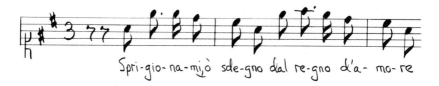

I Rvat, Barb. lat. 4208, ff. 79v-80, anon.
I Rc, 2477, ff. 158-161v, anon.
I Rvat, Chigi Q VIII 180, ff. 32-32v, anon. (Marco Marazzoli).
B Bc, F. A. VI 38, ff. 133-136v, anon. (the attribution Marco Marazzuoli
   is a later addition).
I Rvat, Chigi Q IV 11, ff. 89-92v, Marco Marazzoli.
I MOe, Mus. G. 117, Marco Marazzuollo.
Another version for soprano solo:
I Nc, 33.4.17, I, 91-94, Mario Savioni.
A third version for soprano solo:
P La, 47-I-65, 8v-10, anon.

388.   Sta forte, mio core, nel primo desire. Gh. 236.

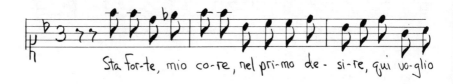

I Rvat, Barb. lat. 4200, ff. 49-50, anon.
Another setting for soprano solo, musically related to the composition
   cited above:
I Nc, 33.4.7, ff. 85-86v (incomplete), Carissimi.
I Rc, 2478, ff. 106-111v, Marc'Antº Pasqualini.
I Nc, 33.4.12, I, 143-148v, Pasqualini.

389.   Su la base di costanza la mia fede inalza. Wo. 156, Gh. 239.

F Pthibault, Rec. H.P.7, ff. 1-16v, Luigi Rossi (the attribution is not in
   the hand of the text, but seems to be contemporary with it).
GB Och, 951, ff. 52-62, luigi (the attribution is not in the hand of the text).
I Nc, 33.5.27, ff. 124-130v, anon.

390.   Su la rota di fortuna posa lieta la mia fè. Gh. 237.

I Rvat, Barb. lat. 4205, ff. 94-97, anon.
I Rvat, Barb. lat. 4220, ff. 101-103v, anon.
I Fbn, Magl. XIX 26, ff. 8v-14v, anon.
I Rvat, Barb. lat. 4208, ff. 80v-83v, MAP.
I MOe, Mus. G. 155, M.A. Pasqualini.
I Rvat, Barb. lat. 4222, ff. 101-105, MAP, text by Giovanni Lotti (arranged
   as a duet; the second voice is a bass.

391.   Su la sponda ove fremea orgoglioso il mar. Gh. 238.

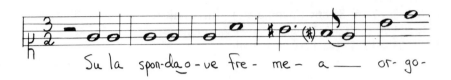

I Rvat, Barb. lat. 4208, ff. 4-8v, anon.

392.   Tanto non v'accostate ch'affè vi bacerò. Wo. 159, Gh. 244.

GB Och, 951, ff. 43-46v, luigi (the attribution is not in the hand of the
  text).
F Pn, Vm7 11c, 37-38v, anon.
B Bc, 15261, pp. 7-8 (copy of 951).

393.   Tanto rigor, perchè, occhi belli amati tanto? Gh. 243.

I Rvat, Barb. lat. 4204, ff. 39-41, anon.
I Rvat, Barb. lat. 4223, ff. 19-20, MAP, text by Nicola Foresta (the text
  begins "Tanto rigor non più non più").

394.   Tormentato mio cor, lascia d'amare. Gh. 245.

I Rvat, Barb. lat. 4208, ff. 16-18v, anon.
GB Och. 953, ff. 46-50, anon.
Another version for solo voice:
I Fc, B3808, ff. 129 ff, Antonio Farina.

395.   Torna in te, che fai, mio core? Gh. 247.

I Rvat, Barb. lat. 4200, ff. 57v-62v, anon.
I SPc, MS 2 (13.905), ff. 9-13v, anon.

396.   Tornate, o miei sospir, pianti e pallori. Gh. 248.

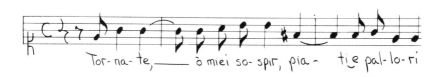

I Rvat, Chigi Q VII 99, ff. 53v-56, Luige Rossi.
I Rvat, Chigi Q VI 81, ff. 0v-3, anon. (Marco Marazzoli).

397.   Trafiggemi, pensiero. Ho perduto un thesoro. Gh. 249.

I Rvat, Barb. lat. 4175, ff. 102v-105, anon.
I Rvat, Barb. lat. 4220, ff. 57-58, anon., text by Giovanni Lotti.

398.   Tu giuri ch'è mio quel seno che vedo. Gh. 252.

I Rvat, Barb. lat. 4200, ff. 50v-52v, anon.
Another setting, for soprano, baritone, and continuo, is attributed to Luigi
   Rossi. See above, no. 260.

399.   Tu mancavi à tormentarmi, crudelissima speranza. Gh. 253.

I Rvat, Barb. lat. 4208, ff. 9-13, anon.
I Rdp, 51, pp. 70-71, anon.
GB Lbm, Harl. 1501, ff. 25v-26v, anon. (lacks the da capo rubric)
I Vnm. It.IV.740 (=10313), ff. 1-5v, M.A. Cesti, *Orontea*, 1649 (lacks the
   2d and 3d strophes).
I Vnm. It.IV.743 (=10317), ff. 21v-27, anon., *Orontea* (lacks the 2d and
   3d strophes).

I Rc, 2464, ff. 13-36v, Carlo del Violino.[5]
I Bc, Q 46, ff. 15v-16v, Carlo Caprioli.
B Bc, 588, no. 3, anon. (copy of Harl. 1501).

The piece is in c minor in all sources except the two Venetian MSS, where it is in a minor.

Gv, I, no. 24, Marcantonio Cesti "verso il 1669."
Pa, II, 35-39, Marcantonio Cesti.

Transcription for string orchestra published from the library of Leopold Stokowski. New York (Broude Bros.), 1949.

It is obvious that Gevaert and Parisotti did not know of the Venetian sources for neither indicates that the aria is from the opera *Orontea*, nor is it likely that either knew of the sources with the attributions Carlo del Violino and Carlo Caprioli. Dr. Albert Vander Linden suggests that Gevaert's source is the MS 588 at the Brussels Conservatory, where *Tu mancavi* follows two cantatas by Cesti, *Del famoso oriente*, copied from GB Lbm, Harl. 1863; and *Sensi, voi ciò che godete*, copied from Harl. 1501, which is also the source for the copy of *Tu mancavi*.[6] Although *Tu mancavi* is anonymous, its inclusion with Cesti's pieces is misleading; it appears as if it, too, were Cesti's. Gevaert's attribution Marcantonio Cesti was probably made on no surer grounds. As for the attributions in the Venetian manuscripts, they are probably incorrect, for *Tu mancavi* does not occur in four seventeenth-century editions of the libretto *Orontea* which I examined.[7] Moreover, Professor Nino Pirrotta and Professor Marcello Pavarini inform me that it is not found in any of the extant musical scores of the opera.[8] Perhaps, as Professor Pirrotta suggests, the aria was inserted in some performance of the opera by a singer especially fond of it, and thus the erroneous attributions in the Venetian manuscripts might be explained. Concerning the composer, it is my opinion that the aria is probably by the Carlo to whom it is attributed in the MSS 2462 and Q 46.

400.   Uccidetemi, affanni, fabri sol di tormenti. Gh. 255.

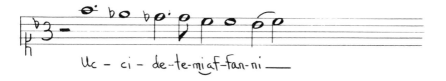

I Rvat, Barb. lat. 4200, ff. 46-47, anon.

401.   Una mano di puro latte combatte. Gh. 256.

I Rvat, Barb. lat. 4208, ff. 144v-147, anon.

402.   Un pensiero che da te, Filli, sen vola. Gh. 260.

I Rvat, Barb. lat. 4175, ff. 27v-29, anon.

403.   Vagabondo pensiero, ove vai? D'onde vieni?

GB Lbm, R.M.24i 11, no. 3, luigi (the attribution is not in the hand of the text).

404. V'intendo, occhi, v'intendo. Voi mi volete morto. Gh. 261.

I Rvat, Barb. lat. 4208, ff. 75v-78v, anon.
I Nc, 33.4.11, no. 42, anon. (in g minor).
US SFdeBellis, MS Misc. V. LXVIII, ff. 21-27, anon.
D Mbs, 1524, ff. 152-155v, anon.
I Rc, 2482, ff. 73v-77, anon.
I Rc, 2479, ff. 193-198v, Carissimi.
GB Lbm, Harl. 1501, ff. 21-23, Carissimi.
Another setting, for tenor solo:
F Pa, M 948, ff. 32v-34v, anon.

405. Vittoria, mio core, non lagrimar più.

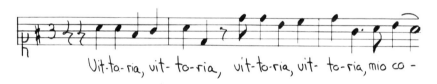

D SW, 4718a, pp. 37-40, Luigi.
I Rc, 2226, ff. 21v-22, anon.
F Pthibault, Rec. H.P. 31, pp. 31-33, anon.
F Pn, Vm7 11c, ff. 46-49, anon.
GB Och, 17, ff. 2v-3, anon.
GB Och, 350, pp. 40-42, anon. (the attribution Carissimi is a later addition
   in pencil).
F Pn, Rés. Vm7 59, ff. 123-124v, Carissimi, text by Domenico Benigni.
I MOe, Mus.G.28, Carissimi, text by Benigni.
I Bc, V/289, ff. 200-202v, Jacomo Carissimi, text by Benigni.
F Pn, Vm7 6, f. 26, Carissimi (incomplete).
GB Lbm, Add. 11608, f. 54v, Carissimi (lacks continuo).
B Bc, F 586 (copy of Add. 11608).

B Br, XY 8286, *Canzonette amorose* . . . (Rotterodamo: Giovanni Van Geertsom, 1656), Basso Continuo part, p. 8, anon.

GB Lbm, and US NYp, *Select Musicall Ayres* . . . (London: John Playford, 1659), p. 66, anon.; also 1653 publication, p. 36, anon.

GB Lbm, and US NYp, *The Treasury of musick* . . . (London: W. Godbid for J. Playford, 1669) I, 66, anon.

Attributed to Carissimi in the following modern publications: E, VI, 20-26; F, pp. 103-108; Gv, I 4-9; J, I, 23-25; N, p. 86; Pa, I, 2-6.

Recording: *Beniamino Gigli singt altitalienische Arien*, Odeon E 90086. Wotquenne lists *Vittoria, mio core* under "Oeuvres douteuses ou apocryphes."

406.   Voi mi dite ch'io taccia. Wo. 167, Gh. 262.

GB Och, 952 (not 947, as Wotquenne and Ghislanzoni indicate), ff. 11-22v, luigi (the attribution is not in the hand of the text).

407.   Voi siete troppo belle, ò mie catene. Gh. 263.

I Rvat, Barb. lat. 4200, ff. 38v-39v, anon.

Another setting for soprano solo attributed to Luigi Rossi, see above, no. 202.

Duets

408.   A chi vive ognor contento ogni mese è primavera. Gh. 264.
       For two sopranos and continuo.

I Fc, D 2357, ff. 31v-33, Luigi. (The text begins "Chi vive ognor.")
I Nc, 22.1.4, ff. 18-21v, Francesco Tenaglia.
D MUs, 4087, ff. 42v-43v, anon.

409.   Ahi, non resta al mio duol altro che morte. Gh. 321.
       For two sopranos and continuo.

I Rvat, Barb. lat. 4200, ff. 172-176, anon.
I Rvat, Barb. lat. 4222, ff. 113-116, MAP, text by Giovanni Lotti.
Eins, 85, 88-89 (copy of 4222), suggests in pencil "Rossi?".
The same music is arranged for two sopranos, a bass, and continuo in:
I Rvat, Barb. lat. 4219, ff. 125-128v, anon.

Ld, I, 95-99 (copy of 4222), suggests, with good reason, that Giovanni
Legrenzi is the composer.[9] His strongest evidence is the opening of the
duet, *Amo più la lontananza*, published by Legrenzi in 1678, which is
very similar to the opening phrase of *Ahi, non resta*. Landshoff would
consider Rossi or Carissimi as the possible composer, except for the fact
that the opening theme spans more than an octave. This he believes to be
a melodic span rigorously avoided by both composers in the themes of
their vocal compositions. There are, however, examples that refute this
assumption; see incipits nos. 2, 28, 78, 146, 158, 125, 180, 260, 266, and
374. Several of Luigi's cantatas open with a melody that is as close to that

of *Ahi, non resta* as the melody from Legrenzi's duet; see above, nos. 7, 43, 158, 165 and 205. The music may be by any one of these composers— or by some other contemporary.
Another setting of the text, for soprano solo:
I Nc, 33.4.7, ff. 37-44, Giovannini.

410.   Amanti, sentite amor che vi chiama. Gh. 267.
    For soprano, alto, and continuo.

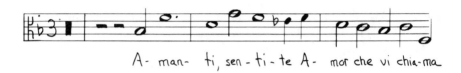

I Fc, D 2357, ff. 150v-152v, Luigi.
GB Och, 350, pp. 53-57, anon.; 377, ff. 12v-17, anon.; 18, pp. 1-4, anon. (the attribution Carissimi is a later addition in pencil); 623-626, part books, anon.; 49, alto part, anon.
I Rvat, Chigi Q IV 85, ff. 33v-36v, anon.
GB Och, 996, ff. 134v-136, Marco.
I Bc, Q 50, ff. 101v-104v, Marco Marazzolli.

Ghislanzoni erroneously read the second voice as a soprano; conse- quently the second voice of the incipit he gives is a fifth higher than it should be.

411.   Armatevi di sdegno, occhi guerrieri. Gh. 272.
    For two sopranos and continuo.

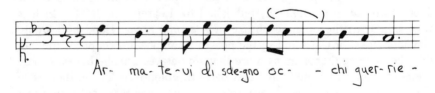

I Rvat, Barb. lat. 4219, ff. 189-191, anon.
I Rvat, Barb. lat. 4204, ff. 118-120, anon.

Concerning Ghislanzoni's description of this piece as a two-voice elaboration of a solo work see above, no. 20.

412.   Che più far degg'io? Ahi, lasso. Gh. 275.
       For two sopranos and continuo.

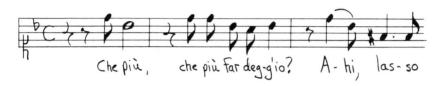

I Nc, 22.5.15, Luigi Rossi.
I Rc, 2464, ff. 109v-115, anon.
I Bc, Q 46, ff. 56-58, Arcangelo.

413.   Ch'io vi fugga, oh questo nò. Gh. 280.
       For two sopranos and continuo.

I Rvat, Barb. lat. 4200, ff. 95v-100, anon.
Eins, 85, 100 (copy of 4200), suggests that Savioni is the composer.
Another version, for soprano solo:
I Rc, 2477, ff. 35-40v, anon.
I Rvat, Chigi Q IV 8, ff. 89-91, anon.

414.   Ciglia brune, archi lucenti mova il ciel. Gh. 60.
       For two sopranos and continuo.

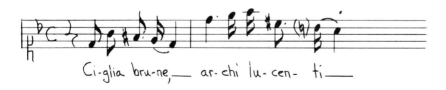

I Rvat, Barb. lat. 4200, ff. 133-142, anon.
Eins, 85, 101 (copy of 4200), adds in pencil "Carissimi!"

415.   Da qual dardo uscì lo strale che mortale nel mio cor. Gh. 285.
        For two sopranos and continuo.

I Fc, D 2357, ff. 111v-113, Luigi.
F Pn, Rés. Vm7 59, ff. 163-164v, Mario Savioni, text by Domenico Benigni. (The text begins "Da qual arco.")
I Bc, V/289, ff. 225-230v, Mario Savione [sic], text by Domenico Benigni.

    —Il mondo della bellezza ha sempre nel sen la congiura.

See above, no. 341.

416.   Lucciolette vaganti che risplendete e non ardete. Gh. 303.
        For soprano, tenor, and continuo.

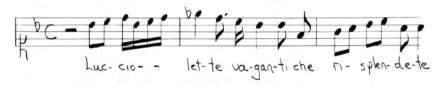

I Fc, D 2357, ff. 173-174v, Luigi.
I Rvat, Chigi Q VI 80, ff. 16v-20, anon. (Marco Marazzoli).
Another setting, for soprano solo:
I Nc, 33.4.7, ff. 95-100v, Mario (Savioni).

417. Luci belle, mio tesoro, pur v'adoro. Gh. 304.
   For two sopranos and continuo in D 2357; for alto, tenor, and
   continuo in Q 48 and Vm7 53.

I Fc, D 2357, ff. 97v-98, Luigi (lacks 5th verse of 2d strophe, and text of
   3d strophe).
I Bc, Q 48, ff. 49v-51, anon. (in C major).
F Pn, Vm7 53, ff. 78-79, Carissimi (in C major; lacks texts of 2d and 3d
   strophes).
Another setting, for solo voice (the voice part is written on the treble
   staff):
GB Lbm, Add. 14336, f 18v, anon. (lacks 2d and 3d strophes; the 3d and
   4th verses of text differ completely from those in the duet version).

418. Mio core, mio bene, languisco per te fra l'onde de pianti. Gh. 305.
   For two sopranos and continuo.

GB Lbm, R.M. 23 f 4, ff. 87-88, Rossi.
I Nc, 22.2.22, ff. 31v-34v, anon. (the attribution Carissimi is a later
   addition).
I Rc, 2464, ff. 100-105v, anon.
I Fc, D 2357, ff. 64-66v, Cesti (not attributed to Luigi, as indicated in
   Ghislanzoni's catalogue).
I Bc, Q 50, ff. 146-148v, Giovanni Marciani.
I Bc, Q 44, ff. 6-8, Giovanni Marciani.

419. Non ho che perder più. Nel mirar il bel tesoro. Gh. 308.
      For soprano, bass (the lower voice is a tenor in MS D 2357, a
      baritone in Q IV 16), and continuo.

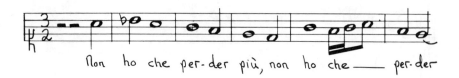

I Fc, D 2357, ff. 143-146, Luigi.
I Nc, 33.5.10, ff. 216-221, anon.
D MUs, 4087, ff. 5v-8v, anon. (lacks continuo).[10]
I Rvat, Chigi Q IV 16, ff. 169-184v, Carlo Rossi.
P La, 47-II-1, ff. 33-42v, Gio. Carlo Rossi.
Another version, for mezzo-soprano solo:
I Nc, 33.4.17, II, ff. 1-4, anon.

420. Non mi fate mentire. Ho già detto a ciascun. Gh. 309.
      For two sopranos and continuo.

I Rvat, Barb. lat. 4200, ff. 176-181v, anon. (lacks text of 2d strophe).
I Rvat, Barb. lat. 4219, ff. 183-187, anon. (The first strophe is a reworking
    of the duet for two sopranos and two basses; the second strophe, the
    text of which is missing, as it also is in 4200, is set for two sopranos
    and one bass.)
Another version, for soprano solo (see above, no. 128):
D SW, 4718a, pp. 95-97, Luigi. (Though there is a definite relationship
    between these two settings, they are not the same.)
A third setting, for soprano:
F Pc, Rés. 2096, pp. 116-117, anon. (lacks continuo).

421. Non più gioie, mio core, a penar, a soffrir. Gh. 311.
      For two sopranos and continuo.

I Fc, D 2357, ff. 6-11, Luigi.
F Pn, Vm7 53, pp. 100-104, Carissimi. (The voice parts are written on
   treble staves; the key is C major. Of the seven sections, the fourth, fifth,
   and sixth are omitted.)

422. Non ti fidar, mio core, chieder gia mai pietà. Gh. 313.
      For two sopranos and continuo.

I Fc, D 2357, ff. 52-53v, Luigi.
I Bc, Q 46, ff. 33v-34v, Carlo Caproli.
I Rc, 2464, ff. 21v-26v, Carlo Caprioli.

423. Occhi belli, s'io v'adoro, se voi soli siete. Gh. 316.
      For two sopranos and continuo.

I Fc, D 2357, ff. 73v-75v, Luigi.
I Bc, Q 48, ff. 81-84, anon.

I Bc, V/289, ff. 267-272v, Carlo Rainaldi.

424.   Occhi miei, voi parlate e sono i sguardi, ohime. Gh. 317.
       For two sopranos and continuo.

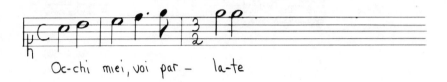

I Fc, D 2357, ff. 94v-95v, Luigi.
I Bc, Q 46, ff. 38-39, Carlo Caproli.
I Rc, 2464, ff. 138-139v, Carlo Caprioli (incomplete).
Another version, for two tenors and continuo:
I Bc, V 195, ff. 36v-37v, anon.

425.   O questo nò, ch'io disperi. Wo. 183, Gh. 322.

Catalogo delle Arie, . . . in manoscritto nella Officina Musica di G. G. I.
Breitkopf (Leipzig, 1765), Parte VIta, p. 35, Rossi. Only the first few notes
of the soprano part are given, with the indication that the piece is for
soprano, bass and continuo. The MS to which the catalogue refers is
unknown to me.

426.   Parla, mio core, che non trova pietà.
       For two sopranos and continuo.

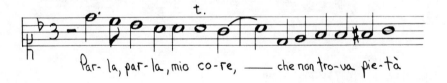

I Rvat, Barb. lat. 4200, ff. 142-144v, anon.
D MUs, 4087, ff. 55-56, anon.
Eins, 85, 104 (copy of Barb. lat. 4200), "Carissimi oder Rossi."

427.   Pensieri, che fate, amor sene viene. Gh. 324.
      For two sopranos and continuo.

I Fc, D 2357, ff. 67-69v, Luigi.
I Nc, 33.4.13, I, ff. 81-90v, Carissimi.
I Rc, 2464, ff. 142-149v, Marco Marazzuolo.
I Bc, Q 50, ff. 83-85v, Marco Marazzoli.
I Rvat, Chigi Q VIII 177, ff. 171v-173, anon. (Marco Marazzoli).
I Nc, 33.5.10, ff. 34-37v, anon.
I Nc, 33.3.1, ff. 117-119v (first soprano), anon.; 33.3.2, I, 50-52v (second
     soprano), anon.; II, 43-44 (continuo), anon.
I Nc, 33.4.14, II, 129-136, anon. (the attribution Provenzale is a later
     addition).

428.   Peregrin d'ignote sponde, se tu giungi ai nostri lidi. Gh. 325.
      For two sopranos and continuo.

I Fc, D 2357, ff. 25v-29. Luigi.
I Rvat, Barb. lat. 4136, ff. 241-258v, anon. (Many of the compositions in
     this MS have concordances with the attribution Carissimi.)
I Bc, Q 50, ff. 59-64v, Carissimi.
Eins, 87, 67-68 (copy of 4136).

429.   Piangete, afflitti lumi, la sventurata sorte. Gh. 326.
       For two sopranos and continuo.

I Fc, D 2357, ff. 195-196, Luigi.
I Rc, 2490, pp. 16-20, Oratio dell'Arpa.

Alberto Cametti, "Orazio Michi 'Dell'Arpa'," op. cit., pp. 241-242, singles out this duet as especially beautiful. He quotes the first fifteen measures.

430.   Piansi già con mesta accento la perduta libertà. Gh. 327.
       For two sopranos and continuo.

I Fc, D 2357, ff. 76-78, Luigi.
I Rvat, Chigi Q VI 81, ff. 157v-163 (begins with the parts exchanged, the first soprano having the line of the second soprano in D 2357), anon. (Marco Marazzoli).

431.   Poiche dal petto mio la piaga ascosa. Gh. 329.
       For two sopranos and continuo.

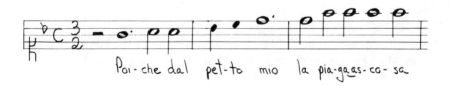

I Fc, D 2357, ff. 70-71, Luigi.
I Bc, Q 46, ff. 39-40v, Carlo Caproli.

432.   Purchè lo sappi tù voglio sempre servire. Gh. 333.
       For two sopranos and continuo.

GB Och, 996, ff. 117v-118, Luigi Rossi.
I Fc, D 2357, ff. 118-118v, Luigi.
D MUs, 4087, ff. 58v and 24, anon.
I Rc, 2505, ff. 169-170, anon.
I Bc, V/289, ff. 273-276v, Carlo del Violino, text by Carlo della Luna.
I Bc, Q 44, ff. 9v-10v, Carlo del Violino, text by Sebastiano Baldini.
I MOe, Mus. F 1263 (in parts), Carlo dal Violino, text by Carlo Luna.
Eins, 85, 54-55 (copy of Mus. F 1263).

Wotquenne lists this work under "Oeuvres douteuses ou apocryphes."

433.   Quasi baleno, in un momento sparì il sereno. Gh. 332.
       For alto, tenor, and continuo.

I Fc, D 2357, ff. 169-170v, Luigi.
I Rvat, Chigi Q VI 81, ff. 166v-171, anon. (Marco Marazzoli).
US SFdeBellis, MS Misc.V.LXVIII, 161 ff., anon. (lacks text of second
    strophe).

In the MS Chigi QVI 81 the music for the second strophe varies somewhat from that of the first strophe; in D 2357 only the text of the second strophe is given without the musical variant.

434.   Se in me talhor volgete, o mia Filli gradita. Gh. 336.
        For two sopranos and continuo.

I Fc, D 2357, ff. 29v-31, Luigi.
I Rc, 2464, ff. 17-21, Carlo Caproli.
I Bc, Q 44, ff. 48v-50v, Carlo Caproli. (The last name is not clearly written; it seems to be Caproli, but it might also be Caprioli. Both spellings are used.)

435.   Son pur dolci a un cor ch'adora le catene.
        For two sopranos and continuo.

Catalogo delle Arie, . . . in manoscritto nella Officina Musica di G. G. I. Breitkopf (Leipzig, 1765), Parte VIta, p. 35, Rossi. Only the first few notes of the first soprano part are given. The MS to which the catalogue refers is unknown to the writer.
D Bds, MS Poelchau 2225, ff. 34ff., Angelo Mich. D. Gasperini, in Venezia, 1695.
Eins, 87, 141-143 (a copy of Poelchau 2225).

Wotquenne lists this work under "Oeuvres douteuses ou apocryphes," indicating that it is attributed to M. A. Gasperini in Poelchau 2225.

Trios and Quartet

436. Io ritorno dal periglio, e nel ciglio porto. Gh. 358.
For three sopranos and continuo.

I Rvat, Barb. lat. 4200, ff. 72v-81, MAP.
Another version, for two sopranos, bass, and continuo:
I Rvat, Barb. lat. 4222, ff. 7-13v, MAP, text by Giovanni Lotti.
I Rvat, Barb. lat. 4219, ff. 85-92, anon.
Ghislanzoni erroneously lists this setting as a concordance of that in Barb.
  lat. 4200. They are two different settings.

The text is published in Giovanni Lotti, *Poesie latine e toscane* (Roma,
1688), II, 116-117.

437. Navicella, che sì altera (Perch'hai grave il sen di vento). Gh. 364.
For three sopranos and continuo.

I Rvat, Barb. lat. 4200, ff. 100v-121, MAP.
I Rvat, Barb. lat. 4219, ff. 59-68v, anon. text by Giovanni Lotti.
Another setting, for soprano solo:
I Rc, 2478, ff. 135-145v, anon.
I Nc, 33.4.14, I, 98-106v, anon. (the attribution Carissimi is a later addition).

The text is published in Giovanni Lotti, *Poesie latine e toscane* (Roma,
1688), II, 33-34.

438.   Per bellezza, per bellezza. Wo. 212, Gh. 369.

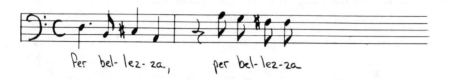

Catalogo delle Arie . . . in manoscritto nella Officina Musica di G. G. I. Breitkopf (Leipzig, 1765), Parte VIta, p. 35, Rossi. Only the first few notes of the bass part are given with the indication that the piece is for alto, tenor, bass, and continuo. The MS to which the catalogue refers is unknown to me.

439.   Piango e nulla alfin mi giova. Gh. 371.
        Piango, prego, e sospiro, e nulla alfin mi giova.
        For three sopranos and continuo.

I Rvat, Barb. lat. 4219, ff. 121-123, anon.
I Rvat, Barb. lat. 4200, ff. 89v-91v, MAP.

Ghislanzoni gives the first incipit taken from the first-soprano line. The lower voices sing, "prego, e sospiro," before the first soprano continues with "e nulla alfin." The result is the second incipit above. (For another example of the same problem, see above, no. 248.)

440.   Io ardo a poco a poco per doi luci homicide. Gh. 300.
        For two sopranos, a mezzo-soprano, a bass, and continuo.

I Rvat, Barb. lat. 4200, ff. 159v-171, anon. (lacks the continuo part after the entry of the bass voice in the third measure; no doubt the continuo player followed the bass voice part).
Another setting, for soprano solo:
I Rvat, Chigi Q VIII 177, ff. 143-144, anon. (Marco Marazzoli).

Notes for Thematic Index 2

1. Pasquale Villari, "Medici," *Encyclopaedia Britannica*, XV, 192.

2. Cametti, op. cit., p. 18.

3. Personal communications from Professor Marcello Pavarini, Dec. 14, 1964, concerning the score of Cesti's opera in the library of the Conservatory Arrigo Boito at Parma, and from Professor Nino Pirrotta, Dec. 16, 1964, concerning the Cesti scores at the Vatican and at S. Cecilia, and the Cirillo version in Naples. (Owen Jander informs me that a seventeenth-century copy of *Orontea* exists in the Pepys Library, Magdalene College, Cambridge. It has not been possible to check this score regarding the point in question.)

4. Other than this attribution there is no evidence that the text is by Gianbattista Marino, for it does not appear in his *La Lira*, 3 vols. in 1 (Venetia: Gio. Battista Ciotti, 1629), or in his *Opere* (Napoli, 1861).

5. Henry Prunières, *L'Opera Italien en France avant Lulli* (Paris, 1913), p. 392, lists *Tu mancavi à tormentarmi* in the "Bibliographie des Oeuvres Connues de Carlo Caproli," giving the sources I Bc, Q 46; GB Lbm, Harl. 1501, and B Bc, 588.

6. Personal communication from Dr. Vander Linden, Brussels, April 21, 1964.

7. *L'Orontea* Drama per musica di Hiacinto Andrea Cicognini da rappresentarsi nel Teatro Grimano di SS. Gio. e Paolo l'anno 1666 (Venetia, 1666), Fbn, 3 E. 7.157. *L'Orontea* Dramma Musicale del Dot. Giacinto Andrea Cicognini; Rappresentato in Firenze nell'Accademia de' Sorgenti (Firenze, 1661), Fbn, 1263-12. *Orontea, Regina d'Egitto*. Drama Musicale del Dottor Iacint'Andrea Cicognini (Torino, 1662), US Wc, ML 48 S 1781. *Orontea, Regina d'Egitto*. Drama Musicale del Sig. Dottor Giacinto Andrea Cicognini . . . (Venetia, n. d.), US Wc, ML 50.2.073C2. Franco Schlitzer, "Fortuna dell'Orontea," *La Scuola Romana*, op. cit., pp. 81-92, lists and discusses the extant libretti of *Orontea*. The writer has not examined all of these libretti, nor the libretto published in 1953 by the Accademia Musicale Chigiana of Siena.

8. Anna Amalie Abert, "Cesti," *MGG*, II (1952), col. 991, states that only fragments of the opera are extant, but Nino Pirrotta, "Tre capitoli su Cesti. II. *L'Orontea*," in *La Scuola Romana* (Siena, 1953), pp. 40-42, gives evidence that three scores are extant in the libraries of the Conservatory Arrigo Boito, Parma; the Vatican (fondo Chigiana), and the Conservatory Santa Cecilia, Rome. (In addition, a seventeenth-century copy of

this score exists in the Pepys Library, Magdalen College, Cambridge University.) Pirrotta says that a great number of the arias are in a volume in the Naples Conservatory library, where there is also a resetting of the libretto by the composer Francesco Cirillo, a contemporary of Cesti. See no. 358, above, where the investigations of Professors Pirrotta and Pavarini are documented.

9. Ludwig Landshoff, *Alte Meister* . . . (Leipzig, 1927), I, Nachwort, pp. 11-12.

10. The indication "Sembrano originali Cantate di Alessandro Stradella" on the first folio of the manuscript is not reliable, for the first four words are not in the hand of the text and seem to have been placed before the attribution Alessandro Stradella at the head of the first piece at a later date. Although no other attribution appears in MS 4087, concordances prove that while some of the pieces are by Stradella, many are by other composers: Luigi Rossi, Cesti, Carissimi, Tenaglia and Carlo del Violino.

Appendix

Fragments from Luigi's Operas Included in Cantata Manuscripts

From *Il Palazzo Incantato*

Armatevi lumi ch'adoro.　　　　　　　　　　　　　　　Soprano solo
　F Pc, Rés. 2096, pp. 82-83, anon. (lacks continuo).

Deh, ferma'l piè fugace.　　　　　　　　　　　　　　Soprano solo
　F Pc, Rés. 2096, pp. 78-82, anon. (lacks continuo).

Donzelle allor ch'udite.　　　　　　　　　　　　Duet for two sopranos
　I Rc, 2480, ff. 297-302v, Luigi Rossi.
　I Bc, Q 44, ff. 30-32, anon.

Dopo l'ombra ecco il sereno.　　　　　　　　　　　　Soprano solo
　F Pc, Rés. 2096, pp. 16-21, anon. (lacks continuo).

Dove mi spingi Amor.　　　　　　　　　　　　　　　Soprano solo
　F Pc, Rés. 2096, pp. 75-76, anon. (lacks continuo).
　I Rvat, Barb. lat. 4175, ff. 45v-49, anon.
　I Rvat, Barb. lat. 4223, ff. 75-79, MAP, text by "N.N.
　　AB" (Antonio Barberini).
　I Rc, 2467, ff. 43v-48, Marc' Ant° Pasqualini.
　Marc'Antonio Pasqualini sang this aria at the first
　　performance; see Ghislanzoni, *Luigi Rossi,*
　　pp. 71-81. The aria is possibly his composition.
　Za, pp. 38-41 (transposed from c minor to b-flat
　　minor).

Qual si sia la tua face, Amor.　　　　　　　　　　　Soprano solo
　I Rsc, G 885, ff. 63-64, del d° (Luigi Rossi).

Se con placidi sguardi.　　　　　　　　　　　　Trio for two sopranos
　I Bc, Q 48, ff. 116-119v, anon.　　　　　　　　　　and a tenor

Si tocchi tamburo.　　　　　　　　　　　　　　　Soprano solo
　GB Och, 949, ff. 55-60, Luigi.
　GB Lbm, Harl. 7549, ff. 28v-29, anon. (lacks continuo
　　and is otherwise a poor copy).
　D Mbs, 1524, ff. 43-47v, anon. (transposed to C
　　major, a whole tone above the original tonality).

F Pc, Rés. 2096, pp. 154-155, anon. (lacks continuo).
GB Lbm, Add. 14336, ff. 12-14, anon. (arranged for
two sopranos; transposed to G major).
F Pn, Vm7 10, ff. 17-18v, anon. (arranged for soprano
and bass).
F Pa, 948, ff. 47v-50v, anon.
US LA MS fC 697, M.4, pp. 94-95 (a fragment of the
voice-part through the eleventh measure), anon.

From *Orfeo*

Al fulgor di due bei rai.   Trio for two sopranos
   F Pn, Vm7 53, pp., 117-120, Luigi   and a tenor
   F Pn, Vm7 6, f. 18, Luigi Rossi (transposed from g
   minor, the original tonality, to c minor).
   US LAu, Special Collections 170/85, ff. 1-8v, Luigi.
   US LA, MS fC 697, M.4, pp. 29-35, Canzone del Sig.
   Luiggi (for soprano and lute).
   I Bc, Q 48, ff. 51v-54v, anon.

Che dolcezza è la certezza.   Duet for two sopranos
   F Pn, Vm7 6, f. 21v. Luigi Rossi.

Da quando un core innamorato.   Soprano solo
   I Vnm, It.IV. 743 (=10317), ff. 41v-44, Luigi Rossi (in
   d minor, a fourth below the original tonality).
   I Vnm, It.IV. 740 (=10313), no. 13, Luigi Rossi.
   Re, pp. 238-239 (lacks continuo).

Il vostro splendore, o luci serene.   Soprano solo
   GB Lbm, Harl. 1273, f. 77v, Luigi Rossi.
   D SW, 4718a, pp. 41-42, Luigi.
   B Br, *Canzonette Amorose*... (Rotterdam: Giovanni
   Van Geertsom, 1656), Basso Continuo part book,
   p. 8, anon.

Mio ben, teco il tormento.   Soprano solo
   D SW, 4718a, pp. 1-3, Luigi.
   F Pn, Vm7 6, f. 17v, Luigi Rossi.
   F Pn, Vm7 17, pp. 96-99, Luigi Rossi.
   I Vnm. It.IV. 740 (10313), no. 15, Luigi Rossi.
   GB Lbm, Harl. 1501, ff. 33-35v, Luiggi Rossi.
   Pm, II, 34.

O, sì, sì, udite!   Tenor solo
   I Vnm, It. IV. 740 (10313), no. 14, Luigi Rossi.

Palme, palme, allori a chi sempre che pugnò.   Soprano solo
   US LA, MS fC 697, M.4, pp. 8-9, anon. (for soprano
   and lute).

B Bc, *Canzonette Amorose...* (Rotterdam: Giovanni
Van Geertsom, 1656), Basso Continuo part book,
p. 6, anon.

Sta saldo, mio core.   Soprano solo
  B Bc, XY 8283, *Receueil des meilleurs airs italiens...*
  (Paris: Christophe Ballard, 1708), III, 228-229,
  anon. (the attribution Luigi Rossi is a later
  addition).

Latin Pieces

Domine, quinque talenta tradidisti mihi. Wo. 222, Gh.   For two sopranos
  380   and two basses
  GB Och, 83, pp. 79-83, Luigi.
  GB Lbm, Add. 31412, f. 71 (copy of Och, 83).

Exulta jubila mater ecclesia.   For two sopranos
  GB Och, 83, pp. 86-89, Luigi.

Floret ager, ridet humus. Wo. 224, Gh, 381, Re. 54.   For soprano solo
  I Bc, Q 45 (not Q 50 as Ghislanzoni indicates), f. 8,
  Luigi.
  B Bc, 17197, p. 182 (copy of Q 45).

Mundi mentes scena volubilis. Wo. 225, Gh. 382, Re.   For soprano solo
  68.
  I Bc, Q 45 (not Q 50 as Ghislanzoni indicates), f. 8v,
  Luigi.
  B Bc, 17197, p. 183 (copy of Q 45).

O amantissime Jesu dilecte mi. Gh. 383.   For soprano solo
  I Rc, 2490, ff. 204-207v, Luigi Rossi.
  Vs, pp. 1-5.

O si quis daret concentum. Wo. 221, Gh. 384.   For three sopranos,
  GB Cfm, 24.F.4, ff. 39v-46, Luigi Rossi   violin, harp and
                                                                 organ

Peccantem me quotidie. Wo. 223, Gh. 385.   For three tenors (not
  GB Och, 83, pp. 84-85, Luigi.   for four voices, as
  GB Lbm, Add. 31412, f. 72v (copy of Och, 83).   Ghislanzoni and
                                                                 Wotquenne indicate)

Summi regis.   For two sopranos
  GB Och, 83, pp. 92-95, Luigi.

Musical Sources

Manuscripts

Austria

Österreichische Nationalbibliothek, Wien.   A Wn
MSS 17758, 17762, 17763, 17765, 18610.

Belgium

Bibliothèque du Conservatoire Royal de Musique de   B Bc
Bruxelles.
XVIIth and XVIIIth century MSS:
FA VI 20, FA VI 23, FA VI 22, FA VI 38, F662.
XIXth and XXth century copies:
586, 588, 660, 663, 664, 11008, 12900, 15258, 15261,
    17192, 17193, 17196, 17197, 28072.

Bibliothèque Royale de Belgique, Bruxelles.   B Br
MS II 3947.

France

Bibliothèque de l'Arsenal, Paris.   F Pa
MSS M.948 and M.152.

Bibliothèque du Conservatoire de Musique, Paris.   F Pc
MSS M.99, Rés. 1357, Rés. 2095, Rés. 2096. H 659,
    vol. II.

Bibliothèque Nationale, Paris.   F Pbn
MSS Vm7 1, Vm7 3, Vm7 4, Vm7 6, Vm7 8, Vm7 10,
    Vm7 11a, Vm7 11c, Vm7 17, Vm7 18, Vm7 53, Vm7
    675, Rés. Vm7 59, Rés. Vm7 102.

Bibliothèque Sainte-Geneviève, Paris.   F Psg
MS 3372.

Bibliothèque G. Thibault, Neuilly.   F Pthibault
MSS G.T.3, Libro di Musica di Salvator Rosa, Recueils
    H. P. 1, 2, 4, 5, 6, 7, 8, 29, 31.

Germany

Niedersächsische Landesbibliothek, Hannover   D HVl
MS IV 422.

Kassel Landesbibliothek.   D Kl
MS 2° Mus. 34.

Lüneburg Ratsbücherei und Stadtarchiv. K.N. 145 Welter S.23.	D Lr
Bayerische Staatsbibliothek, München. Mus. MS 1524.	D Mbs
Bischöfliches Priesterseminar, Bibliothek, Münster (Santini Collection). MS 4087.	D MÜs
Mecklenburgische Landesbibliothek, Schwerin. MSS 4718a, 4718b.	D SW

Great Britain

University Library, Birmingham. MS 5002	GB Bu
Fitzwilliam Museum, Cambridge. MS 24.F.4.	GB Cfm
King's College, Rowe Music Library, Cambridge. MS 22.	GB CKc
Royal Academy of Music, London. MS 107.	GB Lam
The British Museum, London. MSS Additional 14336, 31505; Harley 1264, 1265, 1266, 1272, 1273, 1501, 1863, 7549; RM 24 i 11.	GB Lbm
The Royal College of Music, London. MS 601.	GB Lcm
Westminster Abbey, London. MSS CG 27 and CG 63.	GB Lwa
Bodleian Library, Oxford. Mus. Sch. E 393.	GB Ob
Christ Church Library, Oxford. MSS 17, 83, 350, 377, 946, 947, 948, 949, 950, 951, 952, 953, 959, 996, 998.	GB Och
University Faculty of Music Library, Oxford. MS U. 210. 4.	GB Ouf

Italy

Civico Museo Bibliografico Musicale (formerly	I Bc

Biblioteca del Liceo Musicale), Bologna.
MSS Q 43, Q 44, Q 45, Q 47, Q 48, Q 49, Q 50, V 195.

Biblioteca del Conservatorio di Musica, Firenze.   I Fc
MS D 2357.

Biblioteca Nazionale Centrale, Firenze.   I Fbn
MS Magliabecchi XIX 26.

Liceo Musicale Nicolo Paganini, Genoa.   I Gl
MS A-5-Cass.

Biblioteca Comunale, Macerata.   I MAC
MS Mus. 78.

Biblioteca Estense, Modena.   I MOe
MSS Mus. G 33, G 41, G 42, G 117, G 171, G 172, G
   239, G 279, G 258, G 302, G 307, G 257, G 1263, E
   280, E 300, G 151-159, F 1349, F 1382, Campori
   Y.L.11.g.

Biblioteca del Conservatorio di Musica di S. Pietro a   I Nc
   Majella, Napoli.
MSS 22.1.4, 22.2.22, 22.5.15, 33.2.4, 33.3.1, 33.3.2,
   33.3.11, 33.4.4, 33.4.7, 33.4.12, 33.4.13, 33.4.14,
   33.4.15, 33.4.17, 33.4.18, 33.4.19, 33.4.20, 33.5.10,
   33.5.18, 33.5.27, 33.5.33, 60.1.50, 60.1.51.

Biblioteca del Conservatorio di Musica Arrigo Boito,   I PAc
   Parma.
MS CF-111-1.

Biblioteca Casanatense, Roma.   I Rc
MSS 2226, 2464, 2466, 2467, 2468, 2472, 2475, 2477,
   2478, 2479, 2482, 2483, 2490, 2505.

Archivio Doria Pamphily, Roma.   I Rdp
MS 51.

Biblioteca dell'Istituto di Archeologia, Roma.   I Ria
MS 1.

Biblioteca Nazionale, Roma.   I Rn
MSS Raro 71.9.A.33, Musicale 56.

Biblioteca del Conservatorio di S. Cecilia, Roma.   I Rsc
MS G 885.

Biblioteca Apostolica Vaticana, Citta del Vaticano.   I Rvat
MSS Fondo Barberini latino:

4136, 4146, 4150, 4151, 4163, 4168, 4173, 4175, 4200,
4201, 4203, 4204, 4205, 4207, 4208, 4219, 4220, 4221,
4222, 4223, 4374, 4375.
MSS Fondo Chigiano:
Q IV 2, Q IV 3, Q IV 5, Q IV 8, Q IV 11, Q IV 13, Q
IV 16, Q IV 18, Q VI 80, Q VI 81, Q VI 85, Q VII
99, Q VIII 177, Q VIII 180.

Biblioteca Comunale, Spoleto. MS 1 (13906) and MS 2 (13905).	I SPc
Biblioteca del Conservatorio di Musica "Benedetto Marcello," Venezia. Busta 1-15-N.11 and Busta 16-48-N.47.	I Vc
Biblioteca Nazionale Marciana, Venezia. Codici It. IV-740, 743, 762.	I Vnm
Biblioteca Querini Stampalia, Venezia. MS Cl. VIII, co. 15.	I Vsq

Portugal

Biblioteca da Ajuda, Lisbon. MSS 47-I-65 and 47-II-1.	P La

Sweden

Universitetsbiblioteket, Uppsala. Vok.mus. i hs. 11:9.	S Uu

United States of America

Houghton Library, Cambridge, Massachusetts. MS Mus 106.	US CA
Music Library, University of North Carolina, Chapel Hill. Music Vault M2-1 M1 (formerly in the library of M. Pincherle, Paris).	US CHH
William Andrews Clark Memorial Library, Los Angeles. MS fC 697, M.4.	US LA
University Library, Department of Special Collections, University of California, Los Angeles. MS Special Collections 170/85.	US LAu

Frank V. de Bellis Collection, San Francisco State   US SF de Bellis
   College, San Francisco.
MSS Misc. V.LVIII and Misc. V.LXIX.

Smith College Library, Northampton, Massachusetts.   Eins
Collection of madrigals of the sixteenth and seventeenth
   centuries, copies by Dr. Alfred Einstein, Vols. 85, 86,
   & 87.

   A few of the manuscript sources referred to in the previous catalogues now have new
call numbers. These are listed below to the right of the call numbers formerly used:

B   Bc, 16771=17192; 16772=17193; 16774=17196; 16782=17197; 694=F.A.VI 38.
D   SW, Raccolta VI=4187a.
B   Br, fondo Fetis 2422=II 3947.
I   Rvat, Chigi Q IV 87=Chigi VII 99.
I   Nc, Raccolta 126=33.4.13; 127=33.4.12; 128=33.4.17; 129=33.4.15; 132=33.4.18;
      137=33.4.7; 182=33.5.33.

   The manuscript Rés. Vm7 59-150 at the Bibliothèque Nationale in Paris is referred to in
this catalogue as Rés. Vm7 59. Changing the number for each piece in that source may be
more correct (see the preface to WECIS 2), but it is somewhat misleading. Retaining the
first number and indicating the folios for each piece is a more precise designation since both
the source and the place in it are identified.

Seventeenth- and Eighteenth-Century Publications

Ariette di Musica, à Una, e Due Voci, di Eccellentissimi Autori. Raccolte dal Canonico D.
Florido de Silvestris da Barbarano. Bracciano: Andrea Fei. 1646.

The Banquet of Musick: or a Collection of the Newest and Best Songs Sung at Court, and at
the Publick Theatres. 6 books. London: printed by E. Jones for Henry Playford. 1688-1692.

Canzonette Amorose Libro Primo à Una, Doi, Tre Voci Concertate per Cantare nel Cimbalo.
Spinetta. Thiorba o Altro Simile Instrumento. Rotterodamo: Giovanni Van Geertson. 1656.

Frescobaldi, Girolamo. *Primo Libro d'Arie Musicali per Cantarsi nel Gravicembalo e Tiorba*
a Una, a Dua, e a Tre Voci. Florence, 1630.

Raccolta d'Arie Spirituali à Una, Due e Tre Voci di Diversi Eccellentissimi Autori. Raccolte
e date in luce da Vincenzo Bianchi. Roma: Vincenzo Bianchi. 1640.

Recueil des Meilleurs Airs Italiens Qui Ont Eté Publiés Depuis Quelques Années. Paris:
Christophe Ballard. 1708.

Scelta di Canzonette Italiane di Più Autori. Edited by Girolamo Pignani. London: A. Godbid,
& J. Playford. 1679.

Select Ayres and Dialogues to Sing to the Theorbo-Lute or Basse-Viol... The Second Book.
London: W. Godbid for John Playford. 1669.

Strozzi, Barbara. *Diporti di Euterpe overo Cantate e Ariette a voce sola.* Opera Settima. Venetia, 1659. The print is at Anderson's College, Glasgow Ewing Musical Library, R.C. 17.

References to the libraries in which the above prints can be located are found in the two volumes of the *Répertoire International des Sources Musicales: Recueils Imprimes XVIe-XVIIe Siècles,* and *Recueils Imprimes XVIIIe Siècle.*

Modern Publications

Burrows, David, ed. *The Italian Cantata, I: Antonio Cesti (Wellesley Edition No. 5).* Wellesley, Mass. (Wellesley College), 1963.   *WE 5*

Davison, Archibald T., and Willi Apel, eds. *Historical Anthology of Music.* 2 vols., Cambridge, Mass. (Harvard University Press), 1950.   *HAM*

Dent, Edward Joseph. "Italian Chamber Cantatas," *The Musical Antiquary,* II, 1911, pp. 42-53; 185-199, London (Oxford University Press), 1911.   D

Echos d'Italie. 6 vols. Paris, 185?-187?.   E

Floridia, Pietro (ed.). *Early Italian Songs and Airs.* Vol. I. *Caccini to Bononcini.* Boston, 1923.   F

Gevaert, François Auguste (ed.). *Les Gloires de L'Italie. Chef d'Oeuvres Anciens et Inédits de la Musique Vocale Italienne aux XVIIme et XVIIIme Siècles.* 2 vols., Paris (Heugel), 1868.   Gv

Jeppesen, Knud (ed.). *La Flora. Arie &c. Antiche Italiane.* 3 vols. Copenhagen, 1949.   J

Landshoff, Ludwig (ed.). *Alte Meister des Bel Canto. Eine Sammlung von Arien und Kantaten, von Kanzonen, Kanzonetten, Opern- und Kammerduetten.* 2 vols., Leipzig (C. F. Peters), 1912.   La

Landshoff, Ludwig (ed.). *Alte Meister des Bel Canto. Italienische Kammerduette des 17. und 18. Jahrhunderts.* 2 vols. in 1, Leipzig (C. F. Peters), 1927.   Ld

Neitzel, Otto (ed.). *Gems of Antiquity. Vocal Masterpieces...*Cincinnati, Ohio (The John Church Company), 1909.   N

Parisotti, Alessandro (ed.). *Arie Antiche.* 3 vols., Milano (Ricordi), 1885-1898.   Pa

Prunières, Henry (ed.). *Six Airs et Une Passacaille de Luigi Rossi.* Paris (M. Senart), 1914.   P

Prunières, Henry and G. Tailleferre (eds). *Les Maîtres du Chant.* 6 vols., Paris (Heugel), 1924-1927.   Pm

Riemann, Hugo (ed.). *Kantaten-Frühling*...2 vols., Leipzig (C. F. W. Siegel), ca. 1910.   Rk

Riemann, Hugo (ed.). *Handbuch der Musikgeschichte.* Vol. II, part 2, Leipzig (Breitkopf & Haertel), 1922.   Re

Supplément au Monde Musical, 15 Février, 1913 and 28 Février, 1913, Paris (Imprimerie Roeder).   Su

Torchi, Luigi (ed.). *L'Arte Musicale in Italia*...7 vols., Milano (Ricordi), 1897.   T

Vatielli, Francesco (ed.). *Antiche cantate d'amore.* 3 vols., Bologna (F. Bongiovanni), 1916-1920.   Va

Vatielli, Francesco (ed.). *Antiche cantate spirituali.* Torino (Società tipografico editrice nazionale), n.d.   Vs

Zanon, Maffeo (ed.). *12 Arie Italiane dei Secoli XVII e XVIII.* Milano, 1953.   Za